14 HOU

ANKUR CHAWLA went to school in Delhi and then graduated from the Institute of Hotel Management, Shimla. He was selected as an operations management trainee with the Taj Group of Hotels. He has worked at different Taj properties, including the Taj Mahal Palace and Hotel in Mumbai, for almost five years. Ankur has, over the years, also played musical instruments such as the table and drums, participated in theatre, acted in documentaries and engaged in several public-speaking and marketing engagements. He currently holds a managerial position in the food and beverage department at the Taj Mahal Hotel in Delhi.

14 HOURS

AN INSIDER'S ACCOUNT OF THE 26/11 TAJ ATTACK

ANKUR CHAWLA

RUPA

Published in 2012 by
Rupa Publications India Pvt. Ltd.
7/16, Ansari Road, Daryaganj
New Delhi 110002

Sales centres:
Allahabad Bengaluru Chennai
Hyderabad Jaipur Kathmandu
Kolkata Mumbai

ISBN: 978-81-291-2065-6

10 9 8 7 6 5 4 3 2 1

Ankur Chawla asserts the moral right to be identified
as the author of this work.

Typeset in Minion Pro 11/14.5 by Jojy Philip, New Delhi.

Printed in India by
Thomson Press India Ltd.
18/35, Delhi-Mathura Road
Faridabad 121007

I love you, Mom.

Contents

Prologue

The 105-year-old Taj Mahal Palace and Hotel is the epitome of opulence, luxury, exuberance and dedicated service for the Indian hospitality sector. What Shah Jahan's Taj Mahal is to monuments, the Taj Mahal Palace is to hospitality in India.

I don't want to run through the cliches where I say that I am a normal Delhiite, a guy-next-door sort, that I hated studies since kindergarten, that I was desperate to find a girlfriend, had a badly screwed-up life, etc.; let's get directly to where my shattering, frightening, life-altering experience began. The longest night ever, for me and some hundreds of people across Mumbai, India and even overseas. The most significant milestone of my life's journey, as many would call it.

As a kid, I had two dreams: to either be an actor or an entrepreneur. I was fascinated by the fact that 'introductions' were not meant for actors; any party became successful if they were there, flashing their style statements for the benefit of Page Three, and the icing on the cake was that they were paid well. One couldn't ask for more. Nursing this ambition, I sat for only two entrance exams after school, when my friends were attempting between five to seven, thinking that at least one would click. I sat for a Bachelor's in mass communication entrance exam and the other was, of course, hotel management. However, I was inclined towards the former, reserving the latter as plan B.

On the day of the hotel management exam, I called up Manish (my mentor for the entrance exams) and said, 'Sir, I am sure that I will clear the mass communication exam next month. I don't feel like appearing for this one. What do you think?'

After his refusal to back my decision, I felt I had to sit for the exam. I wasn't aware then that this exam would lead to the most interesting twist in my life.

After wasting three years of my life at the Institute of Hotel Management in Shimla, it was a euphoric moment for me when I came to know that, out of the two hundred-odd students of my batch, I was the only one to get placed as an operations management trainee with food and beverage at the Taj Group of Hotels. Finally, a feeling of not being so wasted after all grew inside me. Every single day became a party until I went to Aurangabad for my classroom training sessions.

After a month of fun and making new lifelong friends and a few classroom sessions, I was chosen as a member of the inaugural team for a new Taj property opening in Trivandrum. This came as a shock to me—I had lived so far on butter chicken but was now being offered a South Indian thali. I was one of those who prefer to die from hunger rather than digest a dosa with sambhar. I just didn't want to go to down south. I read the appointment letter thrice just to make sure that I was not hallucinating.

I almost lost all my hopes with the company and started talking to people from other hotels. But before I could put in my papers as I had decided, Rubal, my classroom trainer, called me. He congratulated me and said, 'Destination Mumbai for you, dude.' He flooded me with a lot of gyan, making sure that my shoulders started feeling the weight of my destiny. I was to be at the famous Taj Mahal Palace at Apollo Bunder!

The thought of savouring vada paav (if not butter chicken) while looking at beautiful girls on Juhu beach made me accept the offer without a second thought. Besides, Mumbai was much closer to Delhi, my home. It looked like the perfect choice for living a perfect life—and maybe getting a perfect girlfriend. And I was excited about the whole thing not only because I had been blessed with a position at the best hotel in the country but also because it was the city of the love of my life—Bollywood.

With crossed fingers and hope in my heart, I sniffed the (not very) fresh air of Mumbai on 14 July 2008. I realized the next week that finding accommodation in Mumbai was more difficult than searching for the Almighty.

On my first day at work, my roommate and I got out of the taxi at the lane behind the hotel. He started moving ahead towards the staff gate while I stood still for a couple of seconds, staring at the walls, relishing the sight of every brick of the hotel. There was something about it which gave me a sense of déjà vu as I walked through the back doors to the learning and development department. I was ecstatic that I was joining the Taj—a prominent landmark for the upwardly mobile. Its grandeur was inspiring.

We were a group of twelve people in the training room. A movie, *Keepers of the Flame* by Zafar Hai, was screened for us. The title was familiar from a couple of albums and a 1942 movie which shared the same title, though I was sure this was not the same one. It was about the history of the Tatas, starting with the family tree and following the journey of the first ever 5-star luxury hotels in India. It was inspiring to watch, how a normal guy with great vision just kept on expanding his business while simultaneously keeping his values stronger then steel. It was a film that did not let us lose interest for even a second. As the movie ended, a tall, charming lady entered the room and introduced herself as Jennifer Green. 'Welcome aboard, guys. I am here for your induction.' She spoke in a soft tone and with a plastic smile as if she was not happy with us coming in or had loads of other work.

Without wasting much time on introductions, she initiated a discussion on the hospitality sector in India, and a history of the Taj group. She told us about the progress of the sector and went on and on and on, spending a good amount of time on a variety of topics. It seemed as if she had been under a lip-binding curse which was broken the moment she saw us. Her extended lecture completely shook up our expectations. No rosy stuff, only practical things which were more or less contrary to what we had thought. She made us feel different and, unfortunately, worse. The partying days are over, dude, I said to myself.

I was just thinking of turning around to see what the others were doing to cope with this excruciating disillusionment, when the guy behind me murmured, 'All that glitters is not gold.' Ms Jenny (that's what we had christened her, seconds after she told us her name), who apparently heard that, gave the poor guy a look so stern that we didn't dare make a sound during the rest of the session. I wondered if she was offended merely at being interrupted, or whether it was the remark itself.

Ms Jenny took us on a tour of the big property, during which she continued her lecture. Nobody knew if she was saying anything productive as we were too busy marvelling at the wonder that is the Taj Mahal Palace. We went through different areas and departments like housekeeping (linen room, laundry), human resources (for formalities), the main kitchen, all food and beverage outlets (restaurants, bars, banquet halls, etc.), as well as the back areas, the swimming pool and gymnasium.

I didn't realize then that this property tour would be so useful in saving lives—mine and others'—one day...

The session ended with a discussion of the history of the property, and the myths associated with it. Someone mentioned that it had been built in a way opposite to how it should have been—the front was supposed to be the back and vice versa. Others mentioned that the architect committed suicide.

All I was sure of was that a new chapter had started in my life and I was going to explore it further. Just how much further was yet to be known.

CHAPTER ONE

9:24 p.m.

The Shooting Starts

The first month after I joined the Taj was the best, and the time that I miss the most. People often call it the 'honeymoon period'—I completely agree. Making new friends, getting to know my colleagues, and that too in a place like Mumbai, had a charm of its own. Mumbai, the city that never sleeps, has the best nightlife destinations that I know of—at least in India. For a person like me, especially, whose last three years had been spent in a snail-paced place like Shimla, this was as if a platter of caviar was being offered to someone who would have been happy to settle for ordinary home-cooked fish.

Once the first month had passed, it was time to roll up our sleeves and get our hands dirty. Things were completely different once we arrived on the actual shop floor. The honeymoon was over; it was time for serious action. We were handed our individual schedules for the coming months and were supposed to go into different outlets accordingly. I started with banquets for a month, followed by in-room dining, and next was the Harbour Bar. The department I enjoyed working at most was undoubtedly in-room dining. I became part of the team almost immediately and never felt like an outsider. Besides, after our shift, every night was a party at the manager's place. Anyway, the training was going smoothly, with loads of learning and a moderate amount of fun.

Pretty son, it was November 2008, my fourth month running. I was working at the Harbour Bar. Though the job was hectic and often exhausting, I loved it because of the feeling of pride and self-worth that came with being part of the management staff at the Taj. For those relatives and naysayers who had earlier considered me on a downhill track to ultimately becoming a glorified waiter—a modernized, English-speaking version of Chhotu from the roadside dhaba—I had come to be no less than the manager of the Taj itself. I was a celebrity to them all—and by celebrity, mind you, I mean Shahrukh Khan, not Rakhi Sawant.

The Harbour Bar first opened its doors to the discerning gentlemen of Mumbai in 1933 and had since then been host to decades of high-powered rendezvous. The bar was L-shaped, with the shorter arm comprising the entrance and the bar counter to the right of it. The longer one overlooked the Arabian Sea and offered a spectacular view of the Gateway of India. The farthest end of it connected to Golden Dragon, a Chinese restaurant. An intimate, classic bar that provided a haven of quiet while affording a glimpse of the vivacity of Apollo Bunder Road, the Harbour Bar was the perfect place to do business or simply relax. It had the distinction of being the first licensed bar in Mumbai, and its decor was heavily influenced by maritime history. Artefacts from sea voyages decked the bar: an anchor, a large compass, binoculars and the all-time favourite American diving helmet—many guests would have their photographs clicked wearing the last. Dimmed lights, serene ambience and understated elegance characterized the bar—it was the best place for relishing the rarest single malts or savouring the finest wines. All this, while watching bustle of the multitudes around the Gateway as people waited for boat rides or fed the pigeons.

On 26 November 2008, I had been working at the bar since noon. Since I was nearing the completion of my tenure there, I was supposed to submit an assignment on the brands, etc., available at the bar. It was a quiet, relaxed evening. People were laughing and the atmosphere was light. I was interacting with the pot-bellied Mr Kirloskar, a loyal visitor to the Taj. He knew all the rumours about the bigshots in the city and was the right person to get all kinds of news and gossip from. However, that evening, we were discussing the selection of malts and the rare collection of other liquors that the bar. Mr Kirloskar was talking about awards won by the bar, the history of the bar, the most popular cocktails and even the personal lives of the bartenders, including me.

'You see that fair lady in the red top at the table close to the right-hand corner?' he suddenly asked, shaking his glass in the woman's direction. I cringed—the gesture could be construed as rude by other people.

'Yes, sir,' I said, trying to hide my excitement at the possibility of finding out the newest secret concealed behind the curtains of beautiful bungalows and swanky high rises. Life at a high-end hotel can be strange—very often, you get glimpses into the lives of the rich and the famous that the common man is never privy to. And I, like many others, could not resist the lure of curiosity about what lay behind the glamorous facades.

'That's Shobhana Lokhande, advocate, and wife of MLA Manish Lokhande,' Mr Kirloskar said. 'I had a very strong crush on her during our college days.'

'And?' I asked, intrigued by this sudden insight into Mr Kirloskar's life.

'And what?' he replied. 'I discovered that she was already dating two guys and I didn't wish her to go to the trouble of accommodating a third one.'

'Maybe it wouldn't have been any trouble at all for her!' I joked. The two of us started laughing.

All of a sudden, I heard a loud bang—as if two heavy objects had collided at a distance. This was not usual. I wondered if it was the sound of the breaking of a bottle of Dom Perignon, the exquisite champagne on display outside the bar—a loss of ₹28,000 on the bottle was the first thing that came to my mind. I was about three feet from the door. 'Excuse me,' I said to Mr Kirloskar, who too seemed astonished and was staring at the door, and took a few steps forward to check what was going on.

I thought with bitter amusement about how the money spent by a rich man on a single bottle of liquor could be used by a poor man to feed his family for a couple of months.

While I was walking towards the door, marvelling at this economic disparity, a man outside suddenly toppled to his side, with his head towards the corridor and legs pointing at the lobby, right in front of me. He was in the corridor outside the bar. He was wearing a white shirt and trousers, and from the way he fell, it looked like he was being chased by someone.

Within seconds, a young guy in a maroon T-shirt and dark-blue jeans came running and halted beside the shivering body of the man who had just collapsed. This second stranger was big-boned and well-muscled. He was wearing a blue cap on his head and had a grey backpack hanging from his left shoulder. He could easily have been mistaken for a tourist had he not been holding a rifle in his right hand. He squeezed the trigger with his index finger and bullets fired with sharp cracks into the body of the man on the floor. He then walked away. The pristine white shirt of the man on the floor started turning red with blood. I could not believe I was not hallucinating.

Working in a hotel prepares you for many things, but not this.

I was in a state of complete shock and for a few seconds I just stood there, completely numb and dazed. I had never seen a person dying or being shot. The man was shivering, trying his best to get up, move his mouth and ask for help, and I couldn't do anything. His eyes were clouded the fear of death— something that would haunt me too for the next many hours.

I started to sense the impending danger to my life and those of the people in the hotel, which made me feel as helpless as the man on the floor. Till that moment, I had never thought of death except somewhere at the back of my mind; now it was a reality to be faced.

The people inside the bar had apparently started speculating about the sound of the shot and were debating over the possible sources of the noise. It was this commotion inside that finally dragged me out of the quagmire of my thoughts. I could only think of running back to the bar. Regular conversation had stopped, the healthy and relaxed environment had turned into a scary zone, just like it happens in Bollywood movies when the villain intrudes into a party at the climax and takes the heroine as hostage. Some people seemed to have figured out that the noise was from a gunshot and this had started to panic the guests.

They were now asking questions. Who was it? Who was shot? Why was he shot? Are we safe?

I sure had no idea.

I could feel everyone's fear. People were staring at me, hoping to get some information about the events taking place outside the bar—and I was as clueless and scared as everyone else.

The first thing that my mind told me to do was shut the door and lock it.

Without uttering even a word, I asked for the bundle of keys from Kevin who was standing behind the bar. 'What's the matter, man?' he asked. I stayed silent for the sake of the guests. I think my silence conveyed to Kevin that I was not in a position to answer, so without further question, he threw the bunch of around twenty keys towards me. For the first time, I got confused between keys—I could not remember which key was for which door. Realizing this, the other steward shouted, 'Ankur, it's 83–84.'

Fiddling with the keys to find numbers 83 and 84, I moved hurriedly towards the door. Sweat was dripping from my temples, unusual in the last week of November. My hands were shivering, but somehow I managed to find the right keys and close the doors. I felt a little more secure after that as I thought that no one would be able to forcibly enter, at least inside my bar. Unfortunately, the feeling was short-lived, as

I realized that the door was mostly glass and could easily be broken down.

I went back to the counter. By now, several minutes had passed since the killing, but no more gunshots had been heard. There must have been a fight between two guests, I thought, which had ended after a couple of shots. I found that the situation was coming back to normal. Though the after-effects were very noticeable, the guests were getting back to their usual chitchat and gossip and were looking relaxed. However, there were a couple of Nigerians who were still very scared. Handing me a credit card, they asked for the settlement of their bill, so that they could leave as soon as possible. The other Indian guests tried to make the situation lighter by saying, 'Don't worry, sir. This is quite common, and the security guys know how to tackle it.'

I took out my handkerchief to wipe the sweat from my forehead and was about to resume my conversation with the pot-bellied Mr Kirloskar, when suddenly the sound of some more shots were heard. These sounds scared one and all who were present. Now everyone knew that it wasn't just a minor skirmish between some guests. Something dangerous was going on and our lives were in grave peril. We could feel the terror inside us. I was not sure whether I would be able to see the sun the next day or not, and I could feel fear not only for my own life but also for the guests sitting inside the bar. I couldn't hide, and the guests were sensible enough to understand that the situation was getting out of hand. Everybody stood up from their couches, alert and holding each other's hands. I am sure most of them were thinking of leaving the place.

The steward gestured to me that the bill for table sixteen

was quite high, and that I must ensure that they did not go without paying. I wasn't very sure of how to respond to that.

Right in front of me was the hotel's phone, the sight of which made me think of informing hotel security at least. I picked up the phone and dialled the security operator's extension.

A lady answered the phone. Before she could even acknowledge my call, I started: 'Hello! There were some gunshots in the hotel. A man was shot just in front of the Harbour Bar.' I spoke in a single breath, as if a delay of even one second would result in several causalities. For a small span of time, I got no response from her. I thought the call had disconnected and I was about to hang up to dial again when she began to speak.

'Give me the details.'

'Yeah, sure,' I said, even though I was in no frame of mind to elaborate on what had happened. All I was looking for was firm and instant action.

'What's your name?'

'Ankur.'

'At what time was the shot fired?'

'Five to seven minutes ago.'

'Where did this happen?'

'Just outside the Harbour Bar.'

'Where were you at the time?'

'I was talking to a guest. Inside. I ran to see what had happened after I heard the sound.' I was getting more and more exasperated with each question—why wasn't she doing anything?

'Did you know the person?'

'What did the killer look like?'

'Where did he go after killing the person?'

I could no longer bear her questioning, like the rapidfire round on *Koffee with Karan*, and I dropped the receiver. I could hear people shouting and the frightening sound of more gunshots.

I turned around to see mayhem inside the bar. Every gunshot fired made men, women and children scream. People were scurrying around, clutching loved ones, trying to find a place where they could at least feel protected, if not find a way to escape.

I thought of peeping outside but could not get myself to move towards the door. I lacked the courage required for that. Not that I was a coward, but I was no soldier either.

After a couple of seconds, I realized that everyone had found a safe corner. The barman and the steward were in the back area and the others including the guests were all in the corner of the bar, hiding behind the couches and the tables. I was standing foolishly, right in middle of the bar, with no clue about what to do next. I didn't come back to my senses till I heard further gunshots. Finally, after this, I too ran towards a corner, thinking that I would be safe there, if only I could reach it before someone barged inside and gunned me down. I focused on the diving helmet and relaxed a bit, thinking that nothing had gone wrong and things would be back to normal soon.

CHAPTER TWO

9:53 p.m.

Initial Move

The Japanese restaurant Wasabi was located on the upper floor of the bar, with the antique spiral staircase as the only way to the restaurant. These stairs were located in the middle of Harbour Bar, though in the corner. They were positioned here due to the space constraints. The idea was proposed when Wasabi opened, and this was the best possible arrangement at the time. Only one person at a time could transit.

After a few of minutes, Vineet (the manager of Wasabi and the ex-manager of room service) came halfway down the staircase and asked me what was happening, though his expression told me that he already knew. He reassured me that everything would be okay and then went back up.

I suddenly heard the screams of a group of people rushing towards the bar; I could hear their screams. The back door of the bar was flung open and many guests, accompanied by the chef from the next-door Chinese restaurant, The Golden Dragon, burst inside. They were all as scared as we were. I still remember all those faces, reflecting the terror that was paralysing minds and bodies. The ladies were crying and holding their children, trying to keep them calm in the middle of the noise. Everyone was crouching and crawling towards the bar from the kitchen entrance. No one knew what was happening right then, or what was going to happen.

The lights were dim, the surroundings felt depressing, the air was heavy with the threat of danger—and we were all helpless. All we could do was pray for our lives. The same question was on everyone's minds. What if we are not here tomorrow morning? What will happen to our family and friends?

I felt transported into a fable I had loved to read and listen to as a kid. In the story, there was this lion that ate up one animal daily, until the rabbit's wit came to the rescue of all the animals. We were all the animals now, and the men with the guns the lions—unfortunately, though, the chances of some rabbit coming to our rescue seemed only as likely as the possibility of that story being true. Our chances of survival were getting slimmer with each passing second.

We were all gathered together in the corner of the bar when Vineet came down the spiral staircase again. 'Let us all move upstairs to my restaurant. You will be much safer there than here,' he said in a commanding tone, looking towards the crowd. He held his cell phone in his right hand.

I don't know how much everyone believed the assurance that they would be safer there, but nobody had the courage to be the first to move. They all stared at each other's faces, hoping that someone would start moving so that they could follow. I had always loathed this habit common to most Indians, of being followers. Very seldom do people make an attempt to create their own individual paths. The individual's prerogative is never that 'individual', actually. I, on the other hand, had always tried to pursue what others termed unconventional. From being the captain of my school's music band to the president of my college's dramatics society, I had always made an effort to be the leader everywhere. And yet, this time around, I was hesitant to make the first move. I was overcome by dilemma, thinking about the pros and cons of this step, trying to come to a decision. The major reason for my hesitation was that one would be visible from the entrance of the bar in order to move towards the staircase.

I had just decided to move when Vineet himself came down. 'Ankur,' he called, waving at me, 'lead everyone to my restaurant.' I climbed up one step of the staircase and turned my face towards the crowd. The looks on people's faces made me feel weak and feverish. 'Please, move up the stairs, everyone,' I said and lowered my head so that I was not exactly face-to-face with them. I could no longer bear to look at them.

After an initial hesitation of a few seconds, some footsteps were heard as, one by one, everyone finally started moving. It was a couple with two small kids who took the initiative, and the rest then immediately followed. Vineet was up at the restaurant's hostess desk to receive them and I was downstairs assisting them to move up.

One of the guests was a bald gentleman in his late seventies, holding his drink in his hand as he moved up the stairs. I had been told about this guy by one of my seniors. All I could remember was that he loved his malts and always came alone. He used to joke around with everyone and was very gregarious and jovial by nature. I assisted him with his glass and told him not to worry about his bill. Given the situation, I was stunned to hear his response: 'Son, tomorrow I may not be alive. This is a beautiful malt, and I don't think I'll get this malt up in heaven or wherever else I go, so please allow me to romance it.'

I stood speechless. I didn't know what to do, so I just saluted him and said, 'Sir, I appreciate your love for the malt. Please carry on.' I was not sure if I did the right thing in allowing him to drink in such a situation, but I felt good doing so. These are the kinds of people who really inspire me. I could see the love and affection he had for the malt. For sure, his wife would be jealous of his malt collection.

Upstairs, from the Golden Dragon's kitchen entrance, some more guests entered, wearing the same fearful expressions. This time, they were accompanied by the restaurant's manager, Saransh, who was my hotel mentor as well. I gave him a brief half smile. 'Ankur, who the hell are you waiting for over there?' he called down the moment he noticed me. He seemed shocked to see me guiding others—I think he was used to thinking of me as a kid. 'Come upstairs, now,' he commanded me. I could not disobey him and finally started to climb the stairs myself.

Wasabi was a contemporary Japanese restaurant which had a contract with celebrity chef Morimoto, also known as the Iron Chef. Wasabi was the first Morimoto restaurant in India and the fourth in the world. Beautiful, elegant, exclusive.

On entering Wasabi, I saw this exquisite place so excessively crowded for the first time. It was so crammed that everyone was trying to find space just for their two feet. Those who are in the field of hospitality assess the place first and then move in. Accordingly, I just stood there to try to understand the place, but the person behind pushed me in. Many people had gathered in a circle near the sushi bar, where a lady could be heard crying her lungs out. I rushed towards the bar, fearing a casualty. Since it seemed unlikely that she herself was hurt, I thought that maybe the man who had been shot outside was her husband or boyfriend.

I stood on my toes to peep over the shoulders of the men in front of me. There was this thin, fair girl with a beaded necklace around her neck sitting at the sushi bar. She was screaming and crying with her mouth wide open. Two middle-aged women, with artificial expressions of concern on their faces, were trying to console and calm her down. 'It's okay, just don't think about it any more,' said the one in front of her. At this, the girl started wailing even louder. It would actually have been funny watching someone her age crying like this had the situation not been so grave. I thought of moving to the bar to give her some assurance as a member of the staff, when I heard many people in the crowd gasp. The girl had fainted. The lady behind her was holding her to stop her from falling backwards on the floor and getting hurt.

'Excuse me,' I said to the person in front of me and tried to make my way towards the bar through the stifling crowd. I signalled the waiter to get some water as soon as I reached the girl. We laid her straight on the floor. 'She saw one of the armed men firing on someone at the entrance. She was here on a date with her boyfriend. They had a fight and he went away. She fears that the terrorists might have shot him,' one of the women said. The waiter came with a glass of water. We sprinkled some on her face and, thankfully, she regained consciousness. She hesitatingly drank some of the water and started crying again.

'Ankur!' I craned my neck to see who had called my name.

It was Arun, one of my colleagues. 'She's fine, let me handle it here. The guests are still coming in. Please go and make them feel comfortable.' I got up and made my way back to the dining area, resisting the push and pull from the crowd once again.

The place was now completely filled with people of all varieties: toddlers, girls, boys, ladies, men and the elderly. Those who a few hours ago had been relishing exquisite and expensive malts and cuisines were praying now to return home safely. The fear and insecurity in the eyes of the bigshots of Mumbai sure was a rare and shocking sight.

There were people lying on the floor and hiding behind the pillars. Some were even hiding behind the counters. I could see a beautiful foreign couple holding each other so tightly that one could feel the depth of love that they shared. There were so many people still coming that we, the hotel staff, had to move to the area behind the staircase, which was just next to the Tatami room. I had not not aware of this area before that day. It was the perfect place for the manager to oversee the restaurant and the main entrance of the hotel. I could see the whole entrance and the main porch of the hotel. It was usually crowded with people stepping out of their chauffer-driven luxury cars; now, there was just one car and a dog. The silence outside spoke clearly of the gory tales of inhumanity that were being written inside the hotel. I could also see one solitary person hiding behind the big planters that were located at the entrance. How terrified he must be feeling, I thought.

Finally, I couldn't bear to be there any more and began to make my way from the restaurant to the kitchens. This involved the difficulty of passing through the crowd, something I didn't want to do at all. More so because of the very recent experience of seeing someone die—I felt almost strangled by some invisible hand.

I collided with innumerable people, including the old guest I thought of as 'the malt amour'.

'Aha! My son,' he addressed me, his facing lighting up. 'I think I forgot my Blackberry on the table where I was sitting. If you and I somehow survive today, then don't forget to find it and give it back to me,' he said, glancing at the glass holding his beloved malt. 'Oh, I think I should find a safe corner before someone bangs into me and spills this,' he said, after someone from behind gave him a little jerk. I saw him saying 'Excuse me' to a couple of people and moving to find a place where he could protect his malt, before vanishing into the crowd. I could not believe this guy. He forgot his Blackberry on the table but brought his drink with him! I am not sure even today if he got his phone back or not.

The kitchens of Wasabi were quite congested due to the space constraints. They were divided into two major sections and the service team also shared the space to store wine and other stuff. The other side of the kitchen opened up towards the back area, making that a transit zone as well. 'Hey Ankur, what exactly is happening outside?' asked one of the chefs as soon as I entered the kitchen.

'No idea, man. I am as clueless as you all,' I answered. This was not true. I was the one who first saw those men killing someone. But I had to say that because I didn't want to talk about it or cause more panic. The chefs in the back area had no information about what was happening in the front. I could hear them speculating. It reminded me of the news channels bullshitting all day long on the smallest and most irrelevant issues. I myself had not had much time to ponder over this, so it was interesting listening to all those tales. Some of them were quite funny.

'It is a gang war, I am telling you. Some party must have been tipped that his bête noire was hiding in this hotel, so he must have sent his men to hunt him down,' said the chef who had questioned me. 'Do you think that Dawood Ibrahim is back?' the one beside him said. 'Could be anyone. Maybe some new guy,' the first chef replied.

'No, I think this must be Shiamak Sinha fighting with Kamal Bawja,' argued the thin, pallid-looking chef who was standing just in front of me. This shocked everyone. Both the men were reputed regular guests. 'What?' he said, seeing the shocked and disapproving faces around him. 'Don't you guys know that the two have been at loggerheads for many years? Kamal used to work under Shiamak a very long time ago, but then something happened and the two parted ways. There has been a Cold War since then. What if that war has turned hot today? I came to know a little while ago that Shiamak used to carry a revolver with him.' It was difficult stifling my laughter at this.

'You all are just talking about some very vague possibilities,' said another chef. 'What you say seems very unlikely. I think it's something bigger. It is an attack on India. An ISI or LeT one.'

'Oh yes. I concur with you,' said yet another chef, joining the discussion. 'It could possibly be an attack. And I feel that this time around Osama Bin Laden might be behind this. He must be pissed off with our country entering into that nuclear deal with the US.'

'But why here in Mumbai?' the first chef whined. 'They should have gone to Delhi. They should have bombed the Parliament instead, where those ministers fought over the deal and finally passed it. Why the hell did these assholes target us?'

'Oh my God! Look at you—almost crying. I was being sarcastic.' The chef who originated the story teased the first one. Everyone laughed at this. I smirked—I could well imagine a particular news anchor, notorious for freaking out audiences over non-existent issues, narrating the attack stories in his trademark animated and exaggerated style.

Thinking of the news anchor, I realized that TV news channels might already have started going out of their way to gain fast TRPs by making unreliable statements over this issue. I decided to call my parents to reassure them. I called up my mother first.

'Hello. You at this time! What's the matter? I was fast asleep,' said my mom's voice from the other end. Hearing it made my mood lighten for the first time in the past couple of hours. Thank God she was not watching TV just then.

'Nothing. I just wanted to inform you that there were couple of gunshots outside my hotel. Things will return to normal very soon. We all are safe. Nothing to worry about,' I replied.

'Gunshots?' Her shock resonated over the phone. 'You're fine? You're sure there is nothing to worry about? Must be a common thing in Mumbai, eh?' She calmed down, gradually.

'Yup, absolutely nothing to worry about. And yeah, a common thing in this city,' I assured her.

'Okay, betaji, take care. Goodnight,' she said, and I hung up the phone.

As my dad was out of station, I wanted to inform him as well. While I was making this call, one of the chefs started looking at me sceptically, as if I were involved with the armed men and informing them about the situation here. Once I realized what he was thinking, I couldn't stop myself and started laughing. What high-voltage drama could have been created, had he made his presumed suspicion public! But leaving that aside, I managed to have a word with my dad, who was more worried than my mom. I had to answer a lot of questions. How did it all start? What did I know? Who shot whom? Why was this happening? Finally, I said, 'Dad, I am safe, you take care, goodnight,' and hung up

There was another chef who was quite excited about all this and wanted to be the first to inform his friends before it became the breaking news of the evening. Pretty soon, we were all chatting on our phones. Probably informing everyone on our contact list. One could hear loud and brash voices saying stuff like: 'Yeah, there was this man. He alone shot around thirty people. Everyone is hiding here and there. I am in the kitchen right now.' Where else does he spend the major part of his day, I thought.

'What the hell are you nutjobs up to?' The yell made us stop our conversations and look towards the back door. It was Chef Sahil, the chef of Wasabi, looking like the most annoyed person on earth. 'God, here we don't even know if we will be alive after the next few hours and you all are busy chit-chatting.' We disconnected our calls and put our cell phones away. This made the situation a little more serious, the way it was supposed to be.

I went to the restaurant again to check out the situation over there. Unfortunately, it was the same—or rather, it was worse. It was terrible to see people crying, especially those whom we think have all the pleasures of life. While leaving their homes everyone would have thought of spending a wonderful evening at the luxurious Taj Mahal Palace and Hotel. Some were there to celebrate, some were corporate guys who had invited their business guests for a meal, and for some it was a dream dinner that they would have saved up for. No one had thought they would end up begging for their lives.

The manager came in with some of the catering assistants. 'Attention, everyone,' he said to the scared crowd. No one listened. 'Attention, please,' he shouted. A few people turned towards him. 'Listen up, everyone, please,' he shouted once more. 'May I please ask you people to clear the area near the bar? Please move a few feet backwards, all of you.' He lifted his arms in the air and gently waved his hands to indicate the desired direction. I, along with the other staff, assisted people in moving backwards. Those who had only just noticed him speaking were asking their neighbours what he had said. A few people who had expected him to announce a way to escape were disappointed. The rest seemed relieved upon realizing that at least it wasn't some bad news.

As the area cleared, the manager and his group assembled in a circle over there. The group remained in conversation for around five minutes. Their voices were hushed to make sure that no one could eavesdrop. Yet, my experience of the past few hours made me guess what the discussion was about. Hence I got busy assuring the guests that everything would be under control soon. Finally, the manager turned towards us and said, 'We shall be evacuating this place and gathering, with the other survivors, at the Chambers in the back area. I am sorry to say that the situation is not showing any signs of improvement. Still, I can assure you all that the Taj is capable of protecting everyone.'

This announcement seemed to bring relief, as everyone felt that at least something was being done for them. People had started discussing the situation among themselves when the manager addressed them again. 'May I request everyone to keep their phones on silent and not panic? Follow me, please, everyone,' he said as he started moving towards the back door.

This was the first time that the guests saw what was on the other side of the door. For them, five-star hotels are supposed to be all shiny and perfect. Believe me, one door can change the world in front of you. It's not that the back areas are not clean or maintained, just that coming from the beautiful restaurants to the back of the house gives one a shock. It was like seeing those virtuous nine-yard-saree-clad bahus in soap operas but getting the shock of a lifetime on seeing them wearing some skimpy outfit on Page Three. Another problem which I could see was that the structure, built approximately 105 years ago, was quite confusing. The lanes were narrow. The chairs, tables, machinery, etc., could not be adjusted properly due to the limited space.

We started moving…

CHAPTER THREE

10:16 p.m.

Further Movement

As we left the restaurant from the back, the kitchen area began. After getting out of the kitchen, right in front was the kitchen stewarding door, with a very old customized elevator on the left. On the right was the long corridor which took one through the entire array of different kitchens on either side, like the room service kitchen, the main kitchen, and Chef Mathur's office on the right. A right turn from there took one towards the Chambers' staff entrance doors.

By now, everyone had assembled near the space in front of the back door. Some people were shifting the chairs to make space to stand. The manager was standing in front. Everyone was looking at him as if they all were schoolchildren on a picnic, waiting for instructions from their teacher.

'Ankur,' the manager called me. I responded instantly, coming out from the crowd and moving towards him. 'Yes, sir.'

'Please move to the end and see that nobody is left behind while I take them to the Chambers back area,' he said. He then turned towards the crowd, saying, 'I am going to take you all to a safer place. Please remember not to panic.' This was the first time I saw all those bigshots listening to somebody so seriously and sincerely.

The manager then opened the door and went into the corridor. Everyone rushed to follow him. The catering assistants helped usher the crowd in. I, the only usher at the end, watched everyone leaving. People were pushing each other in a bid to reach safety as soon as possible. The only life that mattered to them was their own. Scuffling, elbowing each other, they finally vacated the place. They were looking around, surprised to see the back areas of the hotel. I turned around to make sure that no one had been left behind. I moved the tables and couches to check if there was anyone still hiding, went to the bar and even opened the kitchen door and shouted. 'Hello, is anyone there?' a little foolishly, just to make sure that everyone had left for that so-called safe haven. No one was left behind. So it was now my turn to finally vacate the restaurant.

I opened the back door and stepped into the long and crowded corridor. I shut the door behind me and was transported to that corridor of hope, as it appeared in that moment. I saw that the whole area was totally different now. A party was supposed to take place this evening, because of which there were loads of chairs lying around. There were now many, many people standing there as well. I could see people giving directions to each other, but I was sure that no one had a clue about what to do. It was chaos all around.

'Hey, man,' said Rohit, one of the banquet staff, as he came running to me, waving. 'We heard you saw someone dying? Who was it? I mean, how? How exactly did it happen?' he questioned me, barely waiting for the two others following him to catch up.

'Sorry, guys, right now I have been ordered to shift guests to the Chambers comfortably. I'll answer all your questions once I am done with that,' I told them.

'Okay, fine,' Rohit said as he made way for me to move forward. I wouldn't really have minded a discussion with them as I myself was curious to gather some more information to add to what I had seen. But I was scared as hell to be present at a risky place like that when all my colleagues were at the apparently safer Chambers. Moreover, I could see no one else out of all those who had been present back at the restaurant. Reaching the Chambers as soon as possible seemed the best option.

The whole journey to the Chambers was excruciating. I still remember how badly I feared being suddenly hit by a bullet in the back. I kept turning my head to glance at what was happening behind me. All I could see was that most of the people were hurrying to some place or the other and the corridor was gradually getting deserted.

CHAPTER FOUR

10:28 p.m.

In-room Dining

The back door to the Chambers was very small. Only one person could enter at a time, because of which everyone was entering the place in a queue. They all reminded me of my school days, when in the Physical Education period we would make one straight line out of fear of our teacher. The only thing missing now was the 'one arm distance' we had been obliged to keep.

I felt a lot more relaxed when all of the guests went into the Chambers. Finally, a big responsibility was off my shoulders. I felt as if my job was done—getting everyone out of the place that I took care of. I knew it was a little selfish to think that, but the truth was that I was actually thanking God for saving not only me but them as well. I didn't know then that there was a lot more yet to come.

For the last month, my training had been in the in-room dining department, more popularly known as room service. I shared a good chemistry with the rest of the team. To tell the truth, they were the only ones for whom I was actually worried—or, perhaps, at that point of time they were the first and only ones I thought of.

I went inside the department. It too was a mess. All the trolleys in the area were folded and kept on one side in order to make space. Mr Simon, the department manager, was coordinating the situation in there.

I cheered up the instant my eyes fell on him. It was the first time I had smiled since the meaningless blabbering we had indulged in at the Golden Dragon's kitchen. 'Mr Simon,' I called out from behind him. He turned and saw me.

'Oh Ankur!' he said, his expression changing to one of concern as he started walking towards me. He came up to me and hugged me tightly. 'You all right, eh?' he asked when he broke the embrace. 'I was so worried about you. We heard the news that you saw someone getting killed.' I had been about to tell him of my experience, but it appeared that he was already aware of it.

'Yeah, you won't believe what I have been through. I don't know what words to use to describe it.'

'Let me tell you something, buddy. Don't think much about it,' Mr Simon said. 'We'll all be safe and out of this place soon. You just stay positive.' He stroked my hair. His affection for me was clear in his voice. I knew everyone here thought of me and the other management trainees as kids, but some of the people seemed to have special concern for me.

'Yeah, sure, sir. I am more than positive. Trust me,' I assured him.

'By the way, please go and meet everyone around here, especially Surender,' Mr Simon told me.

I gave him a curious look—I didn't know why he wanted

me to meet Surender in particular. Guessing the question that was on my mind from the look on my face, Mr Simon said, 'You will find out why.' He walked away to greet someone who had waved at him from near the entrance.

The tiny IRD cabin was just opposite the kitchen, in one corner of the department. At any given point of time, there were only two order takers who could sit there. More than three people, and the place would become congested. The cabin also had a couple of computers and the Infogenysis machines for conveying the orders to the kitchen.

Right now, there were two order takers; one was crying and other one was trying to calm her. Another front-office girl was in the cabin as well; she too was crying. Surender was trying to crack silly jokes, as usual, to try to make the situation a little better.

'Hey!' said Vineet and gave me a pat on my back. He already knew of my experience as he had been there at Wasabi, and he said in typical Mumbai style: 'Iski to phat gayi'. I smiled weakly. He looked at the front-office girl. 'Why are you crying?'

She turned to us. 'I was coming down after escorting a guest to his room on the fifth floor. When the elevator doors opened, I saw a dead body, blood covering the face, just outside.' She was crying so hard that she could barely speak. 'Bullets had punctured several holes in his body. Blood was oozing out of them.' I shuddered as I remembered the body I had seen. 'I have never seen a sight as gory as that,' the girl continued. 'I was too terrified to even breathe for a few moments. And then I heard the noise of gunshots and the elevators doors automatically closed and I came running over here.'

'Do you know who the person outside the lift was?' Surender asked.

'No,' she replied. 'He didn't look like anyone I knew. And anyway, his face was completely smeared with blood.'

She was calming down slowly after telling us the entire story. Surender looked at me and so did Vineet. The focus was now on me. 'Sir, your turn now,' said Surender. 'What's your story?'

I told a them little bit about my experience. The mood until now had been comparatively light as we were trying to add a bit of humour to the situation. But then Vineet got serious and said that Surender had seen the worst. He asked Surender to undo his coat buttons. I couldn't believe that I hadn't noticed it till now, but his whole shirt was red with patches of blood. Everyone except me had heard about this already. I hugged Surender tight. My breath quickened. I could hear the sound of my heartbeat. I was praying for everyone's safety.

Shamiana was one of Mumbai's favourite coffee shops. It was located diagonally across the entrance of the hotel, to the left, which means it was on the lane parallel to the other restaurants: Harbour Bar, Golden Dragon and Masala Kraft. The place was quite big, offering a view of the pool on one side and adjoining the lobby on another.

Now Surender told us the things that we hadn't known about. That the attacks started in Shamiana. Some guy just started firing inside the restaurant, and a couple of people were injured. During this, one of our very old associates, Mr Rehman, was hit by a bullet. Surender had just entered the hotel at that time. While he was coming for his shift after changing in the lockers, people had been carrying Rehman's body from the back doors of Shamiana, and Surender tried to help. They kept the body outside in a car but had to run back as it was not safe over there either. During this whole fracas, the blood from Rehman's body got on Surender's shirt.

CHAPTER FIVE

10:44 p.m.

Live Action

'Hey, Ankur, we heard that you are stalking some girl these days?' Vineet started his favourite activity—pulling my leg—just to lighten the mood.

'Hey, people,' called out a male voice came as the door opened. Everyone turned towards the door to see the new entrant. It was Manoj, the manager of the butlers. 'Oye, Big B, welcome. Come join us,' we said. He was known for constantly imitating Amitabh Bacchhan, which is how he got this nickname.

'Sorry, guys, I am not here to join you. Rather, I have come to...' He paused for breath. 'I have come to ask you people to vacate this place as soon as possible.'

'Vacate this place as soon as possible!' Surender repeated, stunned. He glanced at the people surrounding him, who also wore expressions of astonishment on their faces.

'But...' Vineet started to speak, but was interrupted by the sound of urgent discussion as a group of people approached the door. It was a group of chefs who had come from the kitchen.

'We need to vacate this place right now. We have to assemble at the Chambers back area. This place is not considered safe any more,' said the fat chef who was standing in the front of the group.

'And who is making these decisions as to which place is safe?' Vineet asked, irritated by the idea of leaving our current hideout.

'You'll get to know everything very soon. Please vacate this place now,' the chef said.

'Vineet, let's go,' Surender said before Vineet could say anything further.

We moved out of the little room and went through the main kitchen leading to the Chambers back area. Every step had some new shock to offer us. Once we came out of the cabin of the room service department, I could see a couple of commandos dressed in black assisting everyone to move out. There were people standing in front of the chef's cabin, trying to peep inside to watch what the news channels were showing. I tried to peep in as well and was surprised to see that most of the channels had reporters outside the hotel. Needless to say, this increased my curiosity as well and I also tried to see whatever I could, standing on my toes and craning my neck. First, I saw a famous female news correspondent speaking in her trademark fiery and aggressive style, standing with her back to a rowdy-looking crowd. I am no lip reader, so I could not understand what she was saying. I got bored and decided to walk back; it was getting really difficult to keep standing on my toes. I was about to turn around and go when, to my surprise, I saw almost all the eyes around me glued to the television screen. Everyone was trying their best to manage a better view of what was happening inside the cabin. This prompted me to push forward and crane my neck again to see what had caught everyone's attention.

The channel, I saw, was running random clips of commandos, police vans, people and soldiers running outside the premises of a huge building. The camera then focused on the building. There was a huge fire at one of the windows. It took me a few seconds to realize that it was none other than the Taj Palace. My hotel! How come I hadn't recognized it before? Had I become completely muddled due to all the shocking events of the night?

It is exciting, I suppose, when on what you thought was a normal evening you become part of an incredible turn of events. But I was coming realize that what is exciting in the eyes of the casual observer outside soon turns into bone-chilling terror for the people actually involved.

Crew from all the major news channels were outside the hotel—this was clearly the breaking news of the evening. Some of the channels were running ticker tapes that termed this incident a 'gang war'. But we, on the inside, were still not clear about what was actually happening.

We finally got to know that the same kind of thing had happened at the railway station and then at Cafe Leopold and also at the Oberoi Hotel at Marine Lines. The situation was clearly far more serious and and a lot bigger than what we had thought.

One of the chefs turned off the television set; he feared that it would spread paranoia among the guests. The crowd started dispersing from outside the cabin area within moments.

'I still don't get what exactly happened,' said one of the trainees.

'Neither can I, dude. I guess none of us can really figure out what has been happening,' Surender said.

Everyone in the corridor was discussing the night's events, trying to reach a logical conclusion over the whole thing. Within the next few minutes, our phones started ringing, one after another. Friends, family, all our near and dear ones, who had come to know about the incident. My batchmates from other Taj properties were calling up to ask about my safety. They also told me about the situation at their end. The other properties in the city, I got to know, and even outside the city, were now on high alert.

John, one of my colleagues from the same property, had asked me in the morning to go with him for a day's outing; I had said no. He too called.

'Hey, Ankur, have your ass on fire, eh?' he said. 'I told you to come with me, but you are so stubborn. Now repent.'

'It's not like that, dude. Everything here is fine and under control.' I was trying my best to sound normal.

'Oh, really? As if I don't have a TV! You know, we had so much fun today. And now I am relaxing at home, watching all this stuff on TV. And I'm thanking God for saving me from all this by giving me the idea of taking the day off. You, on the other hand, are stuck in that life-threatening mess because you are such a loser.' Just that moment, the call somehow got disconnected. I was glad that it did.

He was right, though, I thought to myself. I was starting to feel even worse after the conversation. I really was an idiot for having refused his offer to go with him. However, I wanted to stay positive. John was the idiot for thinking that it was great watching all this on TV—I was lucky to be seeing all this with my own eyes and yet being safe.

I called John back. 'You know what, I am actually the lucky one.'

'What?' He was puzzled.

'I am getting to see all this live, while you are only seeing it on your TV screen. You don't realize how adventurous it is over here,' I bragged.

'Adventurous? Are you kidding me?'

'You missed a lot by not coming to the hotel today, dude. Ha, ha, ha.' The call got disconnected again.

I had never known that I was capable of teasing a person for being left out of such a terrible situation, for not being on the inside. I was amazed that I could feel good about it for even a minute, even though I could sense the wrongness of it all as well. And I was also feeling curiously guilty. My mind was in turmoil.

I put my phone on silent mode so I could avoid answering any more annoying or unsettling calls. Then I went back to the group still huddled together. I realized suddenly that a couple of my batchmates, Shivendu and Micky, were also in the hotel. When I called them, they were not able to talk much. All they said was, 'We are both together and still safe in the back area. We were in the banquet halls. A function was going on, and both of us were allocated to it.'

Then, out of nowhere, two huge, well-built men arrived amidst us. They had long rifles in their hands and were accompanied by one of the hotel's security guys. I could see the anger in their reddened eyes. Their demeanour and their grip on their rifles clearly told of their determination to not come back without killing someone—the terrorist, I hoped. As they walked in, everyone automatically made space for them. I could see that everyone admired and was reassured by their appearance and the gleam of determination in their eyes. They are the experts, I thought. As soon as they left, everyone's eyes again turned back to the news on the television. It was almost like the India-Pakistan World Cup final, where groups of people could be seen standing together, their eyes glued to one small TV at the roadside general store. This time, however, it was not a cricket match. This was much more serious— our lives were at stake. Even the luxury of watching TV was allowed to us for only a couple of minutes more as the cable lines were disconnected in order to reduce the panic amongst the people crowding there.

Disappointed, we all stood there for some time, looking around while the seniors ran here and there, trying to get the situation under control. We still had no idea of what was going to happen next. All we could do was just pray to God for everyone's safety.

'You people are blocking the way.' Several top executives from the management had joined us. 'Move out of here, please,' one of them said to us. 'Go to the Chambers. Or wherever. But do not block this way.'

Everyone instantly obliged. We started moving down the corridor to go to the Chambers, led by two hotel officials. It had got extremely crowded in the corridor. There was hardly any space between two people, so naturally the movement was very slow. Everyone was looking nervous. Their voices and gestures spoke of nothing but fear.

We had not traversed even one quarter of the total length of the corridor when we suddenly heard a deafening explosion. The next instant, the corridor reverberated with screams. All movement stopped. Everyone was wondering what to do and where to go. The women and children started crying. The men present trying to soothe them. I had never seen people look so frightened. I had gone, in the span of a few hours, of having only vaguely thought about death to realizing what the fear of death actually was.

'Please don't stop. Move to the Chambers. Come on, quickly. As fast as you can.' The officials leading the crowd were shouting loud enough to be audible over the screaming and the crying. They started moving again, and the people in the front of the crowd literally ran behind them. I nearly tripped over one a shoelace that had come untied. I was not in a position to bend and tie it up. All I could do was rush, trying to avoid tripping. The situation almost resembled a stampede.

CHAPTER SIX

11:12 p.m.

The Chambers

A private members-only club, the Chambers was where the who's who of the city—even the country—could often be found. This included business tycoons, foreign dignitaries, politicians, advocates and so on. It was located in the Tower wing and comprised conference halls, a bar and a lounge to sit back and conduct informal meetings. Outside the Chambers was the terrace just above the main entrance to the hotel. From the terrace, one could see the Gateway of India against the backdrop of the unending ocean. Entering through the small back door of the Chambers, one arrived at the guest corridor. On the left side were doors to different conference rooms and on the right, just next to the door, were the washrooms. After these was the reception, and then the glass-walled lounge and the terrace.

I entered the Chambers in a state of pure nerves. One side of the small corridor stood hotel staff, some trying to arrange water for the guests and some just chatting. To my surprise, there was a long queue of guests right in front of the door. I was rather puzzled by this. I walked in further and realized that they all were standing outside the washroom. It was the same situation with the ladies' washroom as well.

My colleague Rashmi, who was standing in the queue, saw my startled expression and called out to me. 'Boss, don't give us nasty looks. In a situation like this situation it's the best thing to do—go try it yourself.'

What else could I expect them to do, I thought. I knew this was not the time for humour, but I still said to Rashmi, 'Aren't they feeling scared to go inside alone? I am sure you are.'

'Huh?' she exclaimed.

My joke had clearly fallen flat on its face.

I ventured further in. Every one of the conference rooms was overcrowded. I knew some of the guests, and some of them recognized me too. I could the see the hope in their eyes at the sight of me, but unfortunately I was not destined to play the role of saviour. Even I was praying for some angel to appear and save me. I wished I could do something to help, but things were not in my hand. All I could do was console them, tell them that everything would be all right.

I went inside one of the rooms and people began asking me tired and scared questions. 'What's going on?' 'Where exactly did this bomb explosion take place?' 'Isn't there any way we can get out of this place?' 'Is this the best possible place to hide, or can you think of somewhere else?' 'Are we safe?' This last question I found rather silly, given the situation.

Every question was creating more and more pressure on me and making me feel even more helpless about the situation. I know it was not right, but I couldn't stop myself from giving false answers to a couple of questions. Maybe it would help stem the flow of traffic.

One guest asked me if the hotel security guards were armed. For sure they were not, but I knew what people wanted to hear. Another one asked, 'Is this place locked from all the sides? Are there any cops standing in the back areas for protection?' I, very confidently, said, 'Of course, sir.'

I was lying to allay the doubts and fear. But I could not lie to myself. With every passing second, I was beginning to feel that we would never be able to get out alive. There was no one in the back area who even had a stick. The hotel security was not armed. To top it all, the Chambers did not have walls all around—there was only glass outside, which the terrorists could easily break.

I couldn't bear to stand there any longer. I had never expected that I would someday be unable to face the guests. I was about to leave when some more guests joined in. Most of them came from Masala Kraft, the Indian restaurant which was located at the lobby level, just opposite Golden Dragon. It was the same group of people who, on entering the hotel earlier in the evening, had asked for Masala Kraft; I remembered escorting them.

'Hey,' the middle-aged man leading the group gestured to me as we came face-to-face. 'You were the guy who took us to Masala Kraft, right?'

'Yes, sir.'

'Oh! Are you all right, son?'

'Yes, sir, absolutely. Thanks for your concern.'

I felt very embarrassed. I had been planning to leave the Chambers as soon as possible, but I had now been caught.

'You know what happened with us?' asked the man.

'Of course he doesn't. How did you think he would?' the lady behind him said. I figured that she was his wife.

'Will you let me speak?' The man sounded irritated. Now I knew for sure that they were a couple. 'We heard the gunshots and got scared,' he continued. 'We asked a chef about it. He told us that there was a wedding going on, in which some people had fired into the air. He told us not to worry. The very next second, I saw a person with a gun and a bag running across the corridor.'

I listened in silence. I didn't know how to respond.

'I might trust anyone next time but, not a chef!' the man said, perhaps in an attempt to lighten the air.

'No, sir, please do not say that.' I felt compelled to defend the chef. 'He must have thought it was air firing. That is quite common at weddings here.' I wanted smoothe over the lie. I probably didn't even know the chef, but one must always back up one's colleagues.

'Well, maybe,' the man said, sounding doubtful. 'Okay, son, you take care. I need to go to the washroom.' He excused himself. The rest of the group followed him.

Looking all around, I felt especially bad for the foreigners. They were far away from their homes, probably already feeling as if they were on uncertain ground. And then, on top of that, this incident... They must be feeling shattered.

Unable to take all the stress any longer, I headed out of the Chambers. I could hear people talking about providing water and other amenities to the guests. Getting busy with something seemed to be just the right thing at that point of time. I decided to join the crisis management team.

'We will get water and something to eat in order to keep the guests engaged,' said Vineet. 'It'll also give them energy.'

There were a number of water bottles stored in the Chambers back area—we decided to start there. Then we divided ourselves into teams to arrange for food, water, towels and some bedsheets for the guests to wrap around themselves. We had already figured out the water situation. Sandwiches were sourced from the cold kitchen. But the problem was the linen. We could not find much of the stuff on that floor. Some of the staff members including, surprisingly, people from the contractual staff, volunteered to get the linen from the laundry, which was at the basement level, four floors down.

All this might sound very simple, but doing something like this right them was actually a crazy idea. And yet there was some invisible spark within that made us determined to do whatever it took to help the guests.

Chapter Seven

11: 35 p.m.

Bullets and Broken Glass

We were able to arrange all the required material within fifteen or twenty minutes. Everything was soon sorted and we divided ourselves into teams once more to hand out the stuff to the guests. The managers formed a semicircle near the table usually used by the florist and carried on low-voiced discussions. We were trying to understand what the latest decision was. We had been asked not to start with the distribution until the meeting was over.

Most of us were chatting, swapping jokes or calling up friends—we were still trying to act as normally as possible. But behind the casual laughter and jovial tones there was a strong feeling of nervousness, easily visible.

And yet, somehow, we also had this feeling that the police or army would come in soon and the whole drama would be sorted out. Once it came to an end, we too would be evacuated and would be able go back to our own homes. Everyone, including me, was praying to meet his or her family again. Just thinking about home gave me a very satisfying feeling. Though

I had always been a homesick sort, I had somehow never missed my family, especially my mom, during my tenure at the Taj. I had hardly called her up. She, on the other hand, was always after my life, claiming that she knew I was not looking after myself. My dad used to say, 'Son, leave the job and come back whenever you feel like.' He sometimes used to tease me by saying that I should keep a resignation letter ready to give to my boss if he shouted at me. My sister used to say that since I was now in Mumbai she could enjoy all the comforts of home and have fun alone back home in Delhi. In most of her phone conversations with me, she would ask whether I was dating some girl or not. A sister is the best person with whom a guy can share his secrets—unless, of course, the sister has their mother as her confidant.

The faces of my mother, father and sister were looming in front of my eyes. I remembered how Ted Mosby had explained, in season three of *How I Met Your Mother*, that when we are very near death we see or remember the most important and loved people in our lives. It was in those moments that I realized that how very incomplete I was without my family. I missed them so much that it felt like it wouldn't matter if I died after meeting them just once more.

I was suddenly filled with remorse for never listening to my parents, despite understanding the magnitude of every sacrifice they had made for me. I realized how difficult it was being a parent. Perhaps more difficult than finding water on Mars. There is no technology to facilitate parenting. I didn't want to live for myself. I wanted to live for my parents.

These regretful thoughts were interrupted by a phone call. I excused myself and went to one of the corners to attend to it.

It was my neighbour's dad, asking about my safety. 'Ankur, do you work in the same hotel?' he asked.

'I am working at the Taj which is opposite the Gateway,' I said. I could sense his next question.

'Do you work in the old wing or the new one? I hope you are fine?' I don't know why people do not understand that even if the hotel is divided into two wings, it's still the same hotel. 'Just get out of there—there are some terrorists on the property,' the gentleman added.

I was both touched and irritated on hearing this. I don't know why he thought I—or anyone else—would voluntarily stay at the hotel, given the situation. 'Don't worry, uncle, we are all fine. Moreover, we have guards all around us,' I said, hoping that he might have a word with my dad or mom and reassure them.

'Okay, son, take care of yourself. God bless,' he said and hung up.

I received many similar calls in the next few minutes. Some of them were from people whom I couldn't even recall at first. It was good to hear from them after so long—however, the occasion could have been better!

I rejoined my colleagues to find out what the latest news was. Vineet was resting near a couple of boxes of water.

'So do you think…' I was cut short by one of the managers of coffee shop, who came and asked the teams to start with the distribution. The managers' meeting had dispersed and each one had gone off to look after something or the other. I tried to imagine the magnitude of the responsibility they were currently shouldering. They had the unprecedented task of forestalling the deaths of the guests, their juniors and themselves—while keeping everyone calm. It was worse was for those whose families were staying on the property.

The guys started distributing bottled water to the guests. I was kind of trying to avoid this duty because I knew that there would be hundreds of questions from the guests. I would not have any answers for them and would have to lie, which I hated. Still, I wanted to be of help to people at this moment of extreme distress, and this finally gave me the impetus to join in the distribution activity. I picked up a box of bottles. I was about to approach the guests when suddenly another bomb exploded.

We all stopped moving and stood fixed in our places, completely frozen. It felt as if we were not living beings but wax statues from Madame Tussaud's Museum. I lost track of time and my surroundings. My body felt heavy—so heavy that trying to move a finger would have felt like trying to push a truck loaded with furniture. The explosion had felt like it had been on the same floor. And that too somewhere near us. I could feel the vibrations under my feet. I was standing right at the entrance of the Chambers. Everybody started running towards me. By the time I had even thought of turning around and hurrying inside, the running crowd, which appeared to me at that moment like it was being chased by stampeding bulls, pushed me in and closed the door. I couldn't even see the faces of the people whom I bumped into during the mayhem. When my mind came back to its regular state, I found myself standing at one of the corners of a conference hall in the Chambers. I had absolutely no idea of how I had come to be there. I tried to look for my acquaintances in the crowd, but I could not see any familiar faces. I felt as if I had lost the ability to identify faces. All I could see were expressions of horror and all I could hear were muffled screams. I guessed that the explosion had taken place near the tea lounge or perhaps the banquet halls, which were on the same floor and not very far away. People around me were just staring at each other.

A few minutes later, I somehow gathered up my courage and said to the fellow standing beside me, 'Let's move out and check what is happening outside.' The guy stared at me in incredulity, as if I had asked him to touch a venomous snake. Ignoring him, I opened the door slightly and peeped outside. There was nothing outside the Chambers. The corridor was clear. By now some more people, including Vineet, had gathered behind me. 'Let's go outside, dude,' Vineet said, elbowing me. I went outside, and a few others followed.

'What about the people in the Sea Lounge?' asked one of the managers who had come outside with us.

Located on the first floor of the old wing, the Sea Lounge overlooked the Gateway of India. Surrounded by glass instead of walls, it was the best location from which to view the Arabian Sea. The Sea Lounge boasted some of the best and largest selections of tea and coffee, with the pianist across from the entrance of the lounge adding elegance to the whole place. It was also a popular location for 'You See, I See' meetings— pre-arranged-marriage meetings when the guy and the girl see each other formally for the first time, and then decide whether they want to marry or not. Earlier that day, the chef had put out a buffet of chaat and Mumbai bhel.

'Let's go and try to bring them here. At least they will be with us,' replied Mr Nath, our boss. He turned around and started walking towards the Sea Lounge. He was followed by most of the staff members who were present outside. There was an air of eeriness around us. I thought about what would happen if in the next moment the terrorists decide to throw another bomb and it fell on my head. We were walking as slowly as we could cautiously looking around so that we could sense anything unusual. 'Halt, everyone,' Mr Nath said. For a moment, I thought it was some terrorist who spoke. 'I don't think it is prudent for us to walk like this. Let's crawl instead,' he suggested.

We bent down on our knees and started crawling slowly through the back area of the banquet halls. This corridor ran parallel to that of the Sea Lounge. The passage was filled with smoke from the explosion, so we had to cover our faces with handkerchiefs. It felt like we were a rescue operation team, trying to get people out. I could appreciate the point of view of the rescue guys: the responsibility for protecting many lives was heavy on my shoulders.

While we proceeded at a crawl, one of us, Rahul, squatted to see through the windows overlooking the pool. The manager saw that everybody's attention had shifted towards him. 'Don't...' Mr Nath started speaking, and just then we all heard smashing sounds and saw glass splinters flying in the air just above our heads. Bullets had been fired on us from somewhere, breaking the windows, the broken glass from which fell on some of us.

'Everybody down!' Mr Nath shouted. I closed my eyes. I didn't have the courage to open them for the next few seconds. I could hear my heart hammering in my chest. When I opened my eyes another shot was fired—this time, right above me. The glass broke and fell inches from my. Had I been even slightly taller, I would have been lying dead on the floor.

I could see everybody still in their places, gasping and sweating. Mr Nath told us to turn around and go back as quietly as possible. 'Nobody should stand,' he ordered. I could not stop myself from turning around instantly. I was crawling quickly so that I could get out of there as soon as possible. It was the worst moment I had ever experienced.

We all stood together after reaching the service elevators in the back area of the Chambers, thinking about what to do. Finally, someone called the supervisor of the Sea Lounge on her phone while the rest of us prayed for the safety of the Sea Lounge staff. The lady picked up the call and said, 'We are safe as of now, but not for long.' All the glass had been broken, so the staff and the guests were stuck in a room with no walls—anyone could come in at any time.

We wanted to do something, but we were helpless. We informed all our colleagues and friends who were outside the hotel about the dangerous situation in the Sea Lounge. They all assured us that they would tell the security people and make sure that the message reached the right person. I was still worried about this. What if the right person wasn't informed? What if he got involved in some other work? The questions kept running through my mind. I thought of calling another friend of mine to ensure that he too informed the security personnel. I relaxed a little after this, but the general levels of anxiety remained high.

Finally, we thought of sitting down for a while. There was simply nothing else that we could do right now. Some of us had been working since the morning shift and had had to stay on for some reason or the other. I had not been on the morning shift and had come in at around noon; so, for me, as a hotelier, the hour was not too late.

'Hey! I am scared, man,' said a charming female voice. It was Geeta, the supervisor of the minibar department. I don't know why, but all of us smiled when we heard her voice.

'Don't you worry, darling,' Vineet said. 'Either we'll all get out of this place soon…'

'Or go for a trip to hell very soon,' Surender finished.

Everybody smiled and the atmosphere became a little lighter. Gradually, we all started describing our experiences.

The discussion started with Surender. His shirt still had bloodstains, hidden underneath the coat he was wearing. He described how he had heard gunshots on his way in from the lockers, and how he had helped carry Rehman's body.

While he was talking, Vineet got a call from a friend, who lived very close to the hotel. He excused himself and started chatting on the phone while we continued our conversation. We were still discussing Surender's experience when Vineet came back, his eyeballs almost popping out. 'The Taj's dome is no more…' he said.

All of us stared at him, speechless. Everybody was shocked—no one could have imagined this.

'The dome is the logo of the Taj, it's the symbol of the Taj!' exclaimed Geeta.

'But how is it even possible?' asked Simon.

Vineet explained, saying that it could have been the previous bomb blast which brought the whole structure down.

'This is not easy to digest, bro,' replied Simon, and our conversation was resumed.

Some good and some bad incidents were shared, some made us feel more scared, but some made us feel better. Some made us laugh a bit, but some brought tears to our eyes. We spent a great deal of time chatting, relishing what could be our last hours. I don't know why, but remembering it still brings back a cocktail of emotions. I can both laugh and be sad, just by remembering that time. At times, life feels like a movie, and we are all playing roles in it—the world seemed very unreal in those hours.

I realized I was feeling hungry and thought of heading towards the Chambers kitchen with Geeta. I noticed an employee dressed in the lounge's uniform, standing with his back towards us. He turned around and I saw that it was Morgan, one of the oldest employees in the food and beverage service. 'Hey, Ankur! Care for some oranges?' he offered, peeling an orange.

'Of course, I am here for the very reason,' I said, grabbing another orange from the basket. Morgan was looking very tense. I could see that he wanted to say something but was just not able to do so. 'Why are you looking so tense? Don't you worry, we will all be out in some time,' I said. I had never thought that a person like him, someone who looked so composed most of the time, could be so afraid.

'I am not tense because of myself, it's my daughter who is stuck on the third floor in the IT room,' he said in a very low tone.

I had not even known that Morgan had a daughter, let alone the fact that she worked in the same hotel. I didn't want him to realize that. I tried to make him calm down, but somewhere in my heart I also knew that it was not going to help much.

'You can't understand my pain, unless you are the father of a daughter,' Morgan said. He told me a little about his daughter, and how happy he had been the day she got a job in the same hotel. Slowly, tears came out of his eyes as he described the love and affection he shared with his daughter.

What Romeo would love his Juliet more than a father loves his daughter, I wondered. Though I was technically senior to Morgan, I felt very small in the face of his feelings. I couldn't stand there for much longer. I patted his shoulder gave him a hug. 'Don't worry,' I said. 'All our wishes are with your daughter and she will be fine.' I smiled at him and he smiled back, but it had an undertone of fear. I left the kitchen, trying to control my tears.

CHAPTER EIGHT

1:05 a.m.

Lockers and Bloodstains

Suddenly I heard my phone ring. The screen displayed 'Ankita TMPT'. TMPT was short for Taj Mahal Palace and Tower—that's how I used to store all the numbers of my colleagues. I remembered that Ankita was doing night shifts these days, which usually started at around 11 p.m. and went on till the next morning. It was already almost 1 a.m.

'Hey, sweetheart!' said Ankita. That was how she addressed everyone. 'Where are you? I hope you are fine and out of danger. Is there someone else with you as well?' She flooded me with so many questions that I didn't know which ones to reply to first. There was another question ready even before I could answer the first one.

'Easy, girl, easy,' I said. I explained the situation to her and also reassured her about my safety. She was in the basement, she said, hiding herself in the housekeeping office next to the laundry. I could also hear the voices of other colleagues in the background. 'What are you doing in the hotel, you were supposed to come for the night shift, weren't you?' I asked.

'Shut up and come down, I want to see you. I am not feeling good.' Hearing this sentence from Ankita's mouth was unexpected. As it was, I had also started feeling a bit bored, so I considered going down towards the lockers, thinking that it might be a bit safer over there as well. It was the first time I had seen the staircase so empty. It was horrifying. Thank God I had a couple of colleagues with me.

The lockers was a wide area which connected almost every outlet of the hotel. It was quite congested due to space constraints as well as the number of users. When one entered from the main staff entrance (from which we also entered that night), it was only a little wider than a door. As one entered the passage, on the right hand side were the washrooms. Just after that was a huge hall full of steel cupboards. These cupboards were the lockers, and there were about six to eight facing each other in a row, making aisles in the middle. Overall, the place was quite dilapidated and shouted out for renovation. On the extreme right were a couple of rooms with couches, but these rooms were generally occupied by the people who had been working in the hotel for ages—we used to call them the pillars of the hotel.

We reached the lockers and saw a lot of people roaming about. Most of them, as expected, were on the phone, probably talking to their near and dear ones. We went ahead and mingled with the crowd. I could not see Ankita and called her up. 'Hey! Where are you?' I asked. To my surprise, she was hiding in the housekeeping office, which was just next to the lockers, towards the engineering department. 'I am coming,' I told her and started walking towards the office.

Ankita came out of the office and we hugged each other as

if we would never get to hug anyone else after this. However, there was also a feeling of relaxation. 'Why did you come so early?' I asked her. 'Your shift was supposed to start around eleven, wasn't it?'

'I came early thinking it will be safer to reach a little early rather than to come at ten and then maybe wait for some time in the lockers,' she responded.

'Lucky you, babe!' I said, realizing that she had reached the hotel at around 8 p.m. And the entire thing had started just after that. If she had come even half an hour later, or at 10 p.m. as she was supposed to, things would have been very dangerous.

After some chitchat about her shift, she said, 'I am scared. What is happening?'

Ankita had a strong personality and, I believe, a lot of will power. I knew she could have handled it if faced with the truth, but I still gave her some false reassurance. 'Don't worry, this will be over soon.' Just to lighten the situation I added, 'And now you also have my wonderful company, what else could you ask for?'

She smiled, and I smiled back at her. Then, inevitably, we started discussing how we got caught up in this crap. The conversation went on for the next forty minutes or so. All this time, we were sitting on the staircase and gossiping. We were so involved in our own discussion that we—or at least, I— didn't realize that the situation in the hotel was getting worse. But it was great to talk freely.

I suddenly overheard another group of people. They were talking about Rehman. Naturally, my attention shifted to this conversation. My thoughts were now diverted and, coincidentally, Ankita also got a phone call. I wanted to know more, and so joined the other group.

A guy from the coffee shop Shamiana was speaking. 'Normal operations were going smoothly when suddenly we heard the sound of a gunshot from the lobby, followed by screams. We all froze for a couple of seconds, trying to understand the situation, before we heard a big noise from breaking glass—the glass wall behind the duty manager's desk. After that noise, nobody was still, even though we did not know what had happened. Everyone started running like headless chickens. Some of us ran towards the back area through the kitchen and some of us towards the pool. The terrorist came from the lobby and started shooting in the air. It was then that Mr Rehman got hit by a bullet as he could not run at the same pace as the rest of us.'

All of us standing in the group were trying to mentally connect the dots. Another guy asked about the bomb explosion at the outlet. A stewarding guy standing in the corner said, 'Yes, there was an explosion right in the middle of the restaurant. It wasn't that big, but it was enough to scare all of us.'

After Rehman was shot, he lay in the coffee shop, we heard. When the terrorist left, some of the staff tried to move him to a car parked at the staff entrance. He was still alive then. 'We got him to the gate and made him comfortable in the car,' the guy continued. 'But before we could do anything else, we saw three or four people coming towards us with guns in their hands. We were left with no option but to close the gate and come inside, leaving Rehman in the car. I don't think he's alive now.' The guy was unable to stop his tears. I could see that he was feeling really bad and guilty about what he had done.

Though I was not at all in the mood to talk as I was feeling very low, I still felt like calling my dad.

'Hey, Dad, how are you?' I asked in a low tone.

'I hope you are safe?' he asked.

'Of course, Dad.'

Hearing my low tone, he said, 'You do not sound convincing, what's wrong?'

'Dad, don't worry, there are lots of security guards surrounding us outside the staff zone.' I hated having to lie, but I didn't want him to worry.

While this conversation was going on, I saw an outsider in the lockers, shouting for no apparent reason. Everyone was looking at him. 'I'll call you back, Dad. I am safe,' I said and ran towards the lockers.

I was surprised to see the stranger in the lockers. Some thought he was a guest, but I was sure he was not—he was not dressed the right way. I went close to him and saw an old man in faded clothes and a cowboy hat. He had a salt-and-pepper beard and was using a walking stick. People were saying that he could have come through the staff entrance while the gunshots were being fired. I also heard that he was in a state of shock and could not recollect anything. Nobody had a clue about who he was. Nobody even knew when he had entered the lockers.

I don't know how he must have been feeling looking at the suits and ties all around him. For us these outfits might be usual, but for non-hoteliers it's different. The poor chap was not even able to answer when asked for his address. We all thought that somehow we should make the situation a little calmer for him so that he could get out of his state of shock as soon as possible. Suddenly, the whole atmosphere, which had become a bit lighter because so many of us were together and there was no immediate danger, became very depressing. A whole blend of thoughts, emotions and questions started erupting in my mind. I asked myself why we even bother planning for the future when we cannot even be sure of our next moment. How could life be so cruel to us? Did I really want to live if this was what life was like? The thought that we might not live to see tomorrow was really getting on my nerves. I had to get out of there.

I was not sure of where I should go or what I should do. I sat on one side of the lockers and started playing games on my phone. I also called up a couple of my friends back in Delhi. Still, I couldn't rid myself of my inner thoughts. I knew I was looking tense and I think one of the chefs, Vikram, with whom I had worked earlier in room service, saw this. He came to me and said, 'Hey! What's wrong?'

'Hey, chef, nothing much. When did you get in?' I asked as I did not know what he knew of the situation.

Without answering me he asked, very seriously, 'Ankur, is there something that you are hiding?'

'No, Vikram, why?'

'You are looking so tense.'

Without letting me speak, he started consoling me. I felt as if he was my Dad's best friend mentoring me. The situation was a little funny, but I somehow liked it. He invited me to go along with him for a smoke.

I smiled and said, 'Do you really think we can go out of the hotel right now?'

In a very mysterious tone, as if he was in someone in a Bond movie, he asked me to just follow him.

I followed him blindly and we went into the passage behind the lockers. All I could see above were the pipes for water. He took a left turn and we went through some old-style blue wooden doors. We were inside a very small and dark room. I could see only a couple of broken stools, of the sort which one could find at the tea kiosks on the roadside. I had never been here before. This tiny room led to a second room which I found more interesting. There were couple of old colleagues sitting around a carrom board and playing very seriously. Looking at them, I wondered if they were even aware of the attacks in the hotel.

The room was dark except for a bulb hanging right over the carrom board, lighting the faces of the carrom players. One of them looked at us and offered us a place in the game in a wearied manner. 'Come, join us,' he said. 'This might be the last game of our lives.'

Another guy said, 'Don't mind him, he was just kidding. All we want to say is enjoy your life, have fun and achieve something. We are close to our expiry dates, you guys have just started and you have a long way to go. Anyways, why don't you join us for a game?'

Vikram looked at me and I looked back at him. I was thinking that just ten minutes ago I was about to cry in depression and here we were contemplating a game of carrom. It may have felt awkward, but it was not a bad idea. We went for it. Vikram and I were on one team and the oldies were on the other team. I didn't want to say this in front of them, but technically it was the Young Generation versus the Oldies. Vikram lit up a cigarette and the game started.

I was still feeling uncomfortable when the chef said, 'Dude, chill. Carrom is a much better idea than sitting in a corner and crying.'

Suddenly, I agreed with him completely.

We all started to play with enthusiasm and the game became interesting. From the very beginning of the game, we all tried to bag the queen. It was as if the game was all about winning the queen and nothing else. I had always thought that I was a good player, but the competition was tough. I was glad to be on the same team as the Vikram—he was an excellent player and we were winning. Almost at the end, we had two blacks (their team), one white (our team) and, of course, the queen left on the board. It had become as exciting as an India-Pakistan cricket match. I thought that even if I told anyone about this the next day, no one would believe me.

'Yippee! I got the queen!' Vikram shouted.

'No, not yet,' said one of the Oldies. 'You still have the white one to pot.'

Everyone's concentration was on the board and I was about to shoot when, suddenly, another bomb exploded.

This one sounded as if it was right on top of us and we came back to earth. Before anything else could go wrong, I told Vikram that we should run towards the lockers and he agreed. We all ran. I could not even bear to look back as I was scared shitless.

The scenario inside the lockers was even worse—fear was on every face. Everyone was hiding wherever they could find space. I closed my eyes and prayed to God yet again to get us out of this mess.

CHAPTER NINE

2:05 a.m.

Back to the Chambers

There were lots of other people around, but somehow I felt very lonely sitting at the lockers. It was as if I was left out of the crowd. I couldn't resist calling Vineet to ask about everyone's safety. He said that they were all safe, but he was upset with me as I had gone down without informing him. I realized that I should have kept him in the loop, but now it was too late. I was already feeling bad—this made me feel even worse. I couldn't sit there any more, and thought of going back to the Chambers. At the same time, I was also concerned about security.

'Do you think it is a good idea to go upstairs? All the senior staff members are in the Chambers and their chances of getting out of the hotel are probably better than ours, sitting over here and waiting.' I raised the question with one of the staff from room service sitting next to me.

'Well, I think you are right... We should go up,' he said.

We came out of the lockers area and went towards the Chambers via the service elevators. When we reached the right floor, we started hugging each other. It was as if we were all cousins meeting after a long time. Though Vineet greeted me normally, I could sense that he was still angry with me. We started talking. The guys told me about their experiences in my absence and I did likewise.

After a little while, Amit, a friend from Delhi, called me. Before he could say anything, I said, 'Zinda hoon, bhai—I am still alive!' out of frustation. Hearing this, the crowd around me started staring, but a few who knew me smiled. I could hear a bunch of people laughing at the other end of the phone and all the voices seemed to be familiar. I realized that all my hometown friends were sitting together with the call on speaker. For a moment, I felt that it was rude of them to joke around in such a sensitive situation, but eventually it lightened my mood. They were all worried about me and that was the reason they had called me up. Thinking of the situation from this different perspective alleviated my frustration. When people worry about you, it makes you feel special.

Vineet came back to my original location at the florist's table just opposite the elevators and sat down. The discussion was still on. All of a sudden, Geeta asked about Micky and Shivendu, who were hiding in the banquet halls. How could we have forgotten about them? I called Micky up.

'Hey, Ankur! Are you safe?' he asked.

'We are safe over here. What about you?' I replied.

He was hiding in the Gateway Banquet Hall. The Gateway Hall, as the name suggested, overlooked the Gateway of India and enjoyed panoramic views of the sea. It was located in the right-hand corner of the heritage wing. The entrance was through the L-shaped lobby. It shared the kitchen with the Sea

Lounge at the back. The hall was not very big, but it could accommodate between fifty and seventy people.

'Ankur, the scene over here is quite bad,' Micky whispered. 'Since the hall has nowhere to hide, we are hiding behind one another. I could hear the terrorist just outside the door next to me,' he said.

'But what if they come inside? What will you do?' I asked.

'Some of us have chefs' knives in our hands and we have thought of stabbing them in case they come in,' Micky replied.

I remembered that generally during events in the hall, we kept doors open and the keys were always in the banquet office. I asked Micky about the doors and he told me, 'We have tied up the door handles with cloth napkins.'

'What if somebody applies pressure from outside?' I asked. Micky had no answer. I didn't want to scare him—I just wanted him to be more alert.

I also had a word with Shivendu and he told me that there were some people who were trying to look for a way to jump out of the window. It became very difficult to hear him. I could feel that he was shivering. I told them to take care of themselves.

I went back inside the Chambers. Almost everyone was on the floor now, some talking over the phone, some just lying down and praying to God. There was also a group of men standing at the corner and smoking. I saw them and was about to stop them, but then I thought that they might ask where else they could go for a smoke. I didn't have an answer for that, so I thought I should not disturb them in such a difficult situation. I also saw lots of guests who, I think, wanted to ask a many questions, but were stopping themselves from uttering them.

I can remember a young newlywed couple. They were standing in one corner, and the woman had her head on the shoulder of her husband, as if she was telling him that she trusted him a lot and she would not be harmed, God forbid, if something went wrong while she was with him. In return, he was holding her close to show that he would definitely not allow anything to cross him and reach her. I couldn't stop myself from staring at them. For the next couple of minutes, I almost forgot that there was something going on in the hotel and fell in love with this loving couple.

The lady saw me staring at them and she called me. 'Excuse me, may I bother you for a moment?' she asked.

I went to them, thinking that this might not be a pleasant conversation as she had seen me looking at them. Just to change the topic, without even listening to them, I started consoling them. 'Madam, I apologize for the situation and really appreciate your patience and I assure you that we will get out of this very soon.' I also looked reassuringly at the gentleman and said, 'I hope you understand, sir.'

The smiled at me and I was confused. The lady said, 'No, no. Firstly, we are very sure that all the efforts that you all have put in will get us out of this situation. Secondly, I called you as I just wanted to express my appreciation and thank the entire Taj staff for doing so much.'

That felt so good!

'We understand it is not in your hands—thanks anyway,' the gentleman said.

Even today, whenever I feel low or I am in doubt, this couple comes to my mind and that smile acts as a confidence booster.

CHAPTER TEN

2:28 a.m.

Caring for the Guests

I saw people leaving the Chambers from the back door and wondered whether someone was calling them or if something was wrong. I forced myself to step out from inside the four walls as well. I saw the staff heading towards the Garde manger, or the cold kitchen, which was the kitchen nearest to the Chambers. It was located across the corner in the elevated area. It was adjacent to the butchery and the bakery. The kitchen provided all the cold food—such as sandwiches, salads, cold cuts, etc.—for the hotel.

I went inside the Garde manger and saw lots of chefs standing in different sections and working. They had divided their work and were busy with it. The first row was cutting bread into slices, another group was working on the vegetables and another was working on the stuffing for the sandwiches. The entire scene was set as if they were getting ready for a big banquet, or as if there was a big chef competition that was going to take place. Everyone was dedicated to his or her work. People from the service department were helping the chefs in whatever manner they could.

I also thought of involving myself and started helping them stack the sandwiches in trays. Another friend of mine joined me and while stacking the trays grabbed a couple of sandwiches. Seeing this, the chef offered him another sandwich, but he declined.

'Don't be scared,' the chef said. 'Have it if you like.'

I thought this was very generous and unexpected of the chef, but my friend ruined it all by commenting, 'Thanks, chef but I don't like vegetarian...' There was pin-drop silence for a minute, but then most of the people started laughing. The comment was uncalled for, but it lightened the atmosphere.

When the sandwiches were ready to be served, we started transporting them to the Chambers. I saw people taking cushions, pillows, bedsheets and towels in as well. I went with other colleagues to the Chambers back area and picked up some bottles of water and started distributing these among the guests. These small tasks gave us a different kind of satisfaction and also kept us and the guests engaged so that our brains didn't dwell on the situation. A kind of positive vibe started from nowhere and created a kind of aura around us. Slowly, everyone started involving themselves in the operation of distributing.

I saw that one of the banquet boys was not able to balance the sandwich tray properly as it was a little heavier than usual. I went to him and told him to just concentrate on balancing the tray and let me distribute. We had just started when suddenly the whole tray slipped from his hands and onto a beautiful flower vase, resulting in a big noise. People panicked and got up from wherever they were sitting, thinking that a terrorist had come inside. Three or four managers also came running up. Everyone was staring at us.

It was one of the most embarrassing moments of my life. But I couldn't stop myself from smiling looking at the innocent face of the banquet boy, who was almost crying. The poor chap was feeling so helpless that he seemed to be shrinking. I told the other managers to take charge of the situation and took this guy with the tray to the back area.

'Thank God they were not paying for the arrangements, otherwise there would have been a massive complaint,' said the chef and nobody standing there could resist laughing.

It was just a couple of minutes later that we heard another massive blast. But this time it was as if we had become used to this sound. Still, just to cross-check, I went back to the Chambers and saw that the situation was getting out of hand.

I could feel the discomfort in the air as soon as I entered. There were some who had lost hope. The crowd included a few Chambers members, the so-called who's who of the country. These people had been born with the proverbial golden spoon in their mouths and were used to making people run around for them. It was interesting and illuminating to see them so uncomfortable—they were not used to being forced by anyone, and today the usual pampering was also missing.

'Evacuation has started and we are almost free,' one of the guests stood up and shouted. Everybody turned to look at him, but people's expressions remained disbelieving. Looking at me, he said, 'If you think I am lying, go put on the TV and see for yourself.'

I was trying to calm him down when another guest shouted

back at him, saying, 'Though the evacuation has started, the terrorists are still inside the hotel. Nobody knows on what basis this action has been taken.'

All eyes turned towards us with expectation and hope. Suddenly, I could feel a great weight on my shoulders. Not wasting any more time, I ran towards my bosses. Coincidentally, they were discussing the same thing. I stood on the side after informing them of the situation. Listening to their conversation, a couple of things became clear to me. One, that they were not at all sure about who had taken the decision of evacuation. Second, nobody was ready to take the decision to lead the guests out. What if something went wrong? After all, it was not a game, and the lives of people were at stake.

The discussion was still on when I got a call from Ritika, another colleague from the engineeing department. 'Hey, how are you?' she said without even letting me speak. 'People have already started evacuating the place, what are you waiting for? Why don't you join them and get out of the trap?'

Before she could say anything further, I said, 'Look, Ritika, I have no idea about what you are saying. I don't know where evacuation is going on, but it's not that easy for me to just leave this place.' I hoped she didn't take offence at my impatience. I didn't have a television set in front of me, so I didn't know what information the entire world was getting at that point of time.

After talking to Ritika for a while, I returned to find that the discussion on evacuation was still going on.

'Ankur, why don't you take a couple of associates along with you and go inside the Chambers? The guests are bound to create some amount of panic. Try to calm them as much as possible,' said Vineet, showing a lot of confidence in me.

I felt the responsibility of my task as I went back inside the Chambers with two other colleagues. It was a completely different atmosphere. Some of the people were already standing as if they had been travelling and the journey had concluded. Some looked aggressive. Some were just ready to run in whichever direction were directed. Whenever they saw anyone in hotel uniform, their expressions changed—they thought we were there to take them out of the hotel. All eyes were on us, as if we were on the stage and everyone was just waiting to follow our command.

I was almost speechless because I was not ready to handle the situation, but still I managed to speak. 'Please maintain your patience. We are trying to manage the situation as much as possible.'

I don't think this went down very well and I could hear them talking to each other, breaking the silence.

'Please maintain silence. We are already planning your evacuation from this place. Till then kindly cooperate with us,' said the manager from the Chambers in a strong voice.

This worked. The people quietened down, though they were still not looking very happy. I went to him and said in a very low tone, 'There is no plan of evacuation as of now. You just gave them false hope. Why did you do that?'

'If you tell them the real stuff, they won't like it. Lies will make them happy, and that's what they are used to,' replied the manager in a sarcastic tone.

'I cannot understand why people in the same hotel can

evacuate and we are still at the planning stage here,' one of the guests got up and said.

Another one added, 'We are very much closer to the ground, unlike those sitting on the nineteenth floor.'

The manager was about to speak again when I ran out, thinking that I should inform the bosses before he could make any more false statements. I explained the situation to one of the bosses and said to him, 'Sir, I think the guests are right. Can't we just move out of the hotel like people from the nineteenth floor have done?'

'Yes we can,' he said. I waited for the typical 'however' that usually came out of his mouth when he couldn't take a decision but still wanted to be diplomatic. 'However, we are not sure of what will happen to them once they get out of here. Somebody has to be outside to take them to a safe place.'

Listening to our conversation, Chef Mathur said, 'We are already arranging buses to take survivors from the back area of the hotel to Wellington Mews.'

This was great news! Mr Nath looked at me and nodded with a smile on his face, keeping his hand on my head. I felt awesome—suddenly a spark of happiness lit up my heart.

Work was getting distributed, and I could feel that the evacuation would start in the half hour. I was supposed to be part of the crew clearing the way through which the guests were supposed to evacuate. We moved towards the area to be cleared and the passage through which the evacuation was supposed to take place. Surender also joined in and we shifted all the heavy equipment and machinery like mobile warmers, ice machines, etc., and used them to block all the passages other than the one to be used for the evacuation.

CHAPTER ELEVEN

2:55 a.m.

Evacuation Starts

Discussions and preparations were still going on. Most of the managers were busy on their phones; none of them was on a personal call. Everyone was trying hard to make it possible for all of us to get out of the place. One of our managers was in constant touch with another nearby Taj property, Wellington Mews, arranging buses in order to transport the guests to a safe place. Others were seeking help from the Mumbai police for the evacuation. I felt this was a very wise decision, to which little thought was being paid. Chef Mathur was also trying to arrange armed help to get us out of this situation.

Another group was standing just next to the elevator and making a list of all the people who were still stuck inside the hotel. When I heard it carefully, it took me by surprise. The list comprised both the guests and the staff. This might not seem unusual to a non-hotelier, but I had never seen a list with guests and staff names together. While the food and beverages manager was trying to arrange transport, he came to me and asked me for a head count of the entire room. This would tell us how many people needed to be evacuated and how many batches had to be made in order to take them all out to the buses at a given point of time.

Just then commandos came in from the staff entrance stairs, with a couple of senior cops who seemed to be in charge. They had come to confirm that the place was safe and to give the green signal for the evacuation. It seemed as if things were coming together. I could see a ray of hope.

When everything was almost set we were called for a small briefing in order to understand the whole process and make it a success. Everyone stood in a line. A feeling of passion and dedication was in the air. Everyone had the highest levels of commitment for the mission—we were all ready to sacrifice even our lives, if need be.

The briefing started with a small yet practical speech by the bosses, which had a major impact on us, increasing our enthusiasm. 'If hospitality can cross all boundaries and can set benchmarks for the world to talk about, today is the opportunity, guys.' These were words that really moved us. We were told about our duties and positions after discussing the entire strategy for the evacuation. I was sure that this briefing had not been planned for, yet it was one of the most systematic briefings I had ever attended. It was the perfect example of short, crisp and powerful communication. It was not the words that mattered but the energy that seemed to flow into us on hearing them.

Chef Mathur also barged into the briefing and updated us on the current status of the hotel and the entire city. He gave us a snapshot of the events that had taken place in the last few hours. He took just four or five minutes, but he made us understand the gravity of the whole situation. His final lines, which I don't think I will ever forget, were: 'This is not about food and beverage. Neither is this about creating an experience for a newlywed couple, which is what we usually love to do. In the food and beverage industry, for a mistake or bad experience, we have something known as service recovery, but here that concept is absent. This is about life and death. Either you are safe, or you are not there. Today, one wrong action or one mistake by you—and you will not be able to forgive yourself for your entire life for taking away the happiness of loads of people eagerly waiting to see their loved ones. It is not about smiles, it is about heartbeats.'

This was inspiring enough to make us all feel a thrill. Everyone was facing the same unfortunate situation, but Chef Mathur's way of putting it across was an eye-opener. This spark turned into a fire in our bellies and these five minutes motivated us so much that we were not afraid of any damn thing in the world. We all understood the plan and were ready to go and fight for our lives. I felt proud and lucky to be a part of this, something which I am sure nobody sitting in front of their TV sets could have imagined. We all took deep breaths and puffed our chests out. We were remarkably alert, given that it was 3 a.m. I felt as if I was going to war.

The area where the evacuation was to take place was L-shaped, where the longer part of the L was the path coming from the Wasabi back area at one end and the stairs on the other. The path touched the Ballroom back area, the main kitchen and Chef Mathur's office. The smaller side of the L started from the same stairs at one end and touched the Chambers back area door at the other. These stairs went down towards the ground level to the staff gate in the back area of the hotel. The plan was to make a queue and line up from the Chambers back door to the staircase and leave through the staff exit.

I, with another colleague, stood just next to the staircase in a queue. I was standing one step below on the stairs. The queue started from the Chambers back area and continued the whole way till the stairs, where it descended. Associates were standing along the whole way till the staff gate to ensure that every guest reached safely. Just next to me was the mobile food warmer, which was blocking the path from the stairs coming from above. The sequence of the evacaution looked good, and so far everything had gone well.

The inspector wanted to see the entire route, after which he would give the green signal for the evacuation. He went down with his team and vetted the area and came back with an affirmative response. He said that the passage was free of any kind of risk and we could go ahead with the implementation of the evacuation plan. He went inside the Chambers and took note of details like the number of people from the managers. He advised us to divide the entire lot of people into groups in order to reduce the chance of panic amongst the crowd. He made sure that there was no scope for any terrorist interference and reconfirmed with his soldiers that the area was safe. I could see that he was in constant touch with the commandos at the staff entrance through his communication devices. Once he got the go-ahead from all the places, he gave a green signal to the management to evacuate. Everybody took a deep breath and promised themselves to give it their best shot.

We all stood in a line, forming a boundary from both sides in order to direct guests towards the path of freedom. I was just at the corner where the staircase began. I saw the first group come out of the Chambers. The group was led by the inspector and behind him was the food and beverages manager as he was familiar with the property and also knew about the plans for the buses to transport the guests. I wam sure this was the first time the guests saw the back areas of the hotel—they were clearly amazed to see them. Their eyeballs were almost popping out at the sight of everything around them. Their expressions also held the fear that they were carrying with them. For every step that they took, they were thinking at least twice and judging the situation. However, so far everything was going smoothly and the batch was evacuating successfully.

At one point, Surender looked at me and signalled that we could also get out of the place by joining the batch. I was sure that nobody would even come to know about this. And even if someone did, no one would blame us. But somehow we could not do this as we felt it would be very unethical. Besides, looking at the pace of the evacuation, it was just a matter of a couple of hours more. I smiled at him and he did likewise and we went back to work.

In that batch of people was an old lady who was limping a bit and having trouble moving. Surender and I offered her support and helped her down the staircase. She moved ahead and kept one hand on Surender's head and blessed us, saying, 'God bless you, baccha.' Though she spoke in a very low tone, we heard her and felt very happy. Surender just bowed his head a bit and everyone in the queue looked at each other and smiled. This small incident created a whole glow of positive feeling among the group.

After the first batch was evacuated successfully, the inspector came back and told the second group to move. He went inside the Chambers again and came back out leading the second group, who were even more scared. I felt as if all the crying people had been put together into this group. They were all moving very slowly and we had to push them very discreetly. While they were moving, Mr Nath walked in again and started putting pressure on the group to move fast, and surprisingly it worked. 'This is not a marriage reception, it's a bloody evacuation. Treat it like one. Move fast,' he commanded. He was good at putting pressure—it was part of his job.

Somehow, this group was also evacuated. And then came the third group. While they were crossing, one lady's phone rang. Chef Mathur and another manager came running to the lady and instructed not only her but also the entire brigade to switch off their phones. There was a sudden pause among the group. During the evacuation process, I saw some of the older staff leaving the hotel. Observing this, Surender and I looked at each other and smiled. At the same time, Mr Nath came running from the staff gate. Looking at him, we both thought that if a person like him could come back inside the hotel, even though he could have left, then why couldn't we do our small bit? We got motivated again and stood our ground.

CHAPTER TWELVE

3:10 a.m.

Terrorists

Everything was flowing smoothy and batches were coming out and evacuating. Of course, there were some hitches like controlling the noise levels of the guests, moving them at a constant pace, etc. By now we were almost accustomed to this and everything was looking as if it was sorted out. Freedom was just metres away and we felt it would just be an hour or so before we would also be tagged as survivors.

The group in the queue now consisted of the guests and some staff from the Golden Dragon. There was a feeling of trust and hope in everyone's hearts. The old staff of the restaurant were thanking us without speaking: they just nodded at us. We also nodded back with respect. The eye contact seemed to transfer confidence. The restaurant's hostess had tears in her eyes. I have no idea why she smiled when she looked at Surender, but I could not stop myself and I started teasing him.

Suddenly, the feeling of freedom went down the drain and fear took hold once again when, from nowhere, we heard a number of gunshots. In milliseconds, everyone had started running here and there. And the gunshots refused to stop. I realized that the noise was coming from the staircase, from the upper floor. It was not just one or two shots but a continuous stream. For a couple of seconds, none of us could judge the situation. Everyone scattered and tried to find a place for their safety. More than half of the queue ran towards the staff gate, thinking they might be the lucky ones who would manage to leave, and the rest who knew that the risk was too high ran back towards the Chambers.

'Come, Ankur, this way,' Surender shouted and pulled me down towards the staff gate.

'Move,' I replied and ran behind him.

I heard people screaming at the top of their voices. The staircase was very small and congested. It was a bottleneck—everyone wanted to move but couldn't find space. People were pushing each other as much as they could. It was, ultimately, a fight for life. Every gunshot felt as if it was meant for us. I felt as though the shot was right behind me and the next moment I might feel pain ripping through my chest and the story of my life would come to an end.

During this scuffle, the hostess of the Golden Dragon restaurant slipped from the staircase and fell to the floor. Surender and I could see people walking on top of her as they struggled to move ahead. We could still hear the gunshots behind us and, for a moment, we considered leaving her and moving ahead. I looked at Surender and he gave me a positive sign. We picked her up and dragged her towards the end of the staircase, where she managed to start running herself.

We could feel that the terrorists were still on the upper floor. We could hear the noise of shots and screams from the floor above. We all split into groups and some of us ran towards the staff lockers. Another group standing near the Chambers door must have run towards the other side of the stairs or back inside the Chambers.

I was worried about Simon as he was standing right in the middle of the queue. He was not with us and it was likely that he had gone towards the Chambers door; if he had done so, he would be the last one to enter the Chambers. 'Where did the terrorist come from?' I asked Surender.

'From the main kitchen, I think,' he replied.

I said, 'I am sure that one came from the staircase which was behind us and the other one through the main kitchen in order to cover us from both sides.'

Surender agreed and asked, 'What happened to the chefs who were already in the main kitchen?'

'And how about the chefs in the Garde manger?'

Someone standing just next to us said, 'One of the chefs ran towards the main kitchen while the terrorist was coming from the stairs. The chef got stuck and was shot dead by the other terrorist coming from the main kitchen.' This confirmed that there were at least two terrorists.

Morgan, the guy whose daughter was also stuck a couple of floors above, was hiding himself in the Garde manger's deep cold storage area, where the temperature was an unbearable minus four degrees Celsius. This area was used as the butchery storage, with all the meats hanging upside down. He was not alone; a couple of other colleagues were with him. The door to the cold storage had a small window to peep into the room. Sitting amidst all the meats, he couldn't control his curiosity and tried to peep through the window. By tragic coincidence, we later heard, he peeped out just as a shot was fired at the window. The bullet hit his eyeball and killed him. Another chef, who was hiding in the main kitchen under the counters and machines, seemed safe. The terrorist was just leaving when bad luck took the chef's life. His phone started ringing and he was detected by the terrorist behind the counters. Somebody who wanted to ask after his safety became the reason that he lost his life.

CHAPTER THIRTEEN

3:25 a.m.

Hunting for a Hiding Place

We ran towards the staff gate in order to get out of the hotel. Everyone was pushing each other; it was just like the crowds in the Mumbai trains, except that the stakes were so much higher than a seat.

We all went running from the staircase and had the shock of our lives—the exit door for the staff was closed. For a moment, we almost lost hope. The noise of the shots was hitting our ears and the only door out was now closed. The situation seemed dire. Instead of trying to find a way to open the door, we thought it would be wiser to hide wherever we could. We considered hiding in the training department, which was to the right of the gate and a level above. We turned around and had to face another disappointment. The whole staircase was filled with water.

Hearing the gunshots and screams, we realized that we could not stand there for even a second longer. Trying not to lose heart and keep the momentum going, we had to take the risk of crossing the same staircase again, to go towards the staff lockers. I was sure that there were other people hiding there as well. With our fingers crossed and prayers on our lips, we ran towards the lockers. We realized almost immediately that this was a bad decision. The place was seriously overcrowded and people were falling on top of each other.

'Ankur, we will be the last ones to enter the lockers—if we manage to survive long enough to reach the entrance,' said Surender. 'It will take us a couple of minutes to get in and we can't afford that.'

'I agree, but where shall we go?'

Another guy who used to work in banquets said, 'Come this way.'

We had no choice but to follow him. We headed in the opposite direction, with another five or six people joining us. We ran around fifty metres and then the guy leading us turned. We had our doubts about this, but still we followed him as he was the only one who seemed to have a plan in mind. He went inside the linen room and whispered, 'Come here, sir, no one knows about this place.'

It was a completely dark room with all the staff uniforms hanging along its sides. We went in and the people who had followed us came inside as well, making a lot of noise. 'Shut up,' said Surender. 'Don't you dare make noise.' I had never seen him so serious or shouting like this at someone.

Just next to the staff lockers was the housekeeping office, opposite which was a small lane that led towards the linen room. In the corner on the right there was a small counter with a window for the staff to exchange uniforms. It was a big room where all the hotel's linen and uniforms were stored on hangers, with aisles in between for movement. In the middle of the room was an elevated area, which was used as a store for discarded linen and shoes. The room was made of metal, with very small steps that made it quite dangerous. The laundry was connected to the linen room so that there could be a smooth flow during operations.

We started moving inside the linen room, between the aisles, with clothes brushing against us from all sides. We wanted to hide ourselves in the cover provided by the clothes. By slowly bending and walking, Surender and I reached the corner of the room and hid ourselves under the doorman's dress. We sat there and took a deep breath. Then we looked at each other and shook hands. 'We are alive!' said Surender.

I responded in the same tone: 'Yes, we are alive.'

It was very hard to believe that we had escaped death so narrowly.

'Hey, why are you sweating so much?' I asked Surender.

'I was playing soccer,' he replied, grinning, and we shared a smile. 'But why are you sweating so much?' he asked me.

I had no answer. I hadn't realized that I too was sweating profusely.

The room was very hot because of the clothes and the absence of ventilation. We were very, very far from feeling good, and the hot and claustrophobic environment made us feel even more depressed. After a while, we began to think about getting out of there. Given that it was a completely enclosed space and we had no way of escaping if we were accosted there, the place simply did not seem safe enough to hang around in.

'Surender, let's get out of this place and see if we can get into the lockers,' I said.

'No, that would be too risky. Let's sit for a while and then decide,' he replied.

We managed to sit for some more time, but it soon became unbearably suffocating. There was pin-drop silence and we wanted to maintain that. We started moving towards the linen exchange counter. The banquet guys were also hiding there. When they saw us move, they got ready to follow us, even though we ourselves were not sure of our goal.

While we were crawling, we heard the sound of something striking metal. I looked around and asked, 'Is everything all right?' I saw that one of the banquet staff had bumped into the metal staircase which led to the elevated area in the linen room.

'Surender, let's go up there. It's the safest place right now,' I said.

'But what is upstairs? We might get stuck,' he said.

'It's one of those spots that no one will be aware of. Forget the terrorists, even half the hotel is not aware of this place,' I said.

He agreed and we made a plan to move upstairs. One of the guys was deputed to move last; he would keep an eye on the entrance as the rest moved one after the other.

The staircase was very old, traditional-style and almost vertical. Not more than one person at a time could stand on it. It had not been intended to be a permanent structure. The landing was small and opened right in the middle of the room, dividing it into two smaller rooms on either side. The right side was so full with all the discarded material that one couldn't enter the place. On the left side was an ancient fan, right at the entrance; I didn't think it worked any more. As one entered, there was a single bed without a mattress but with two office chairs on top of it. On the other side was a big trolley overloaded with clothes. Behind this trolley was a big pile of linen.

One after the other, we started finding good spaces to hide. Everyone wanted to get as far as possible from the entrance. Surender and I went behind the trolley, thinking it would be best to hide behind the linen. However, two other guys who had climbed up before us were already hiding there. So we had to be in front of them. Two more chaps went and hid themselves behind the single bed. Though we tried to be as calm as possible, we still ended up making some noise. We threw all the linen on top of ourselves in order to make sure that we could not be seen.

The other guys were still but talking about the situation. Before I could say a word, Surender told them to shut up. I just sat there, tired to the core. I tried to relax, but I couldn't help revisiting the situation over and over in my head. I had to pinch myself to convince myself that it was all happening, that we were not simply stuck in a nightmare. I could not believe that a couple of our colleagues were no more.

My mind took me through the sequence of events at the Harbour Bar, Wasabi, the Chambers and then, finally, the evacuation.

Slowly, as I lost myself in my musings, the room quietened. It was still and silent for the next ten minutes or so. Suddenly, Surender's phone vibrated with a message. We were in a different, silent world, and even this small vibration was enough to alarm us.

CHAPTER FOURTEEN

3:50 a.m.

Bomb Blast

After a while, we could breathe easier. Though we knew the situation was likely to be short-lived, we even managed to smile. We felt safe, at least temporarily, and fortunate that we had not been shot during our close encounter with the terrorists.

Surrender looked at me and smiled. 'So...' he said in a very low tone.

'So...' I replied. 'We have to get out of this place too. It's not over yet.'

He was so tired that he just nodded and said, 'Yes'.

There was complete silence for the next fifteen or twenty minutes. We were not in a position to say even a word. I was trying to control the many thoughts revolving in my mind. Surrender got up and inquired about the others who had been with us, including Vineet and Simon. I too had no idea of what had become of them and we were just keeping our fingers crossed. I thought of calling them, but when I shared the idea with Surrender, he stopped me, saying that it might be risky for them to answer their phones. I agreed and had no option but to put my phone away.

We talked in a low voice about our experiences—it still seemed so unreal to us. I told Surender how I and everyone else at the Harbour Bar had thought that the fight was between two guests and would be resolved very soon. That view was quickly turned upside down, and what we had tried to assure the guests was a small thing turned out to actually be a massive, unfortunate and shocking incident. We were somewhere in the middle of our conversation when I received a message from Ritika, saying, 'Everyone including some Golden Dragon staff and our colleagues are out of the hotel, I hope you are among them.' I shared the message with Surender, and he stayed expressionless. He snatched the phone from my hands and typed: 'We were the ones who helped and escorted them in getting out, but unfortunately we couldn't be among them'. He gave me back the phone, asking me to read and send the message. I read it and told him, 'She won't believe me. And even if she does, she will call us fools.' We smiled out of embarrassment. I replied to the message, thanking Ritika for the update and requesting further information.

We started speculating about when we would be able to get out of this mess. Surender said, 'I have to come out of this mess as I promised my parents that we were just waiting for daylight and would be out very soon.' I had also lied to my parents, telling them not to worry about me as there was enough security.

I got really scared when Surender asked me a very valid question: 'What if something had gone wrong with you?' He added, 'You should have told them the truth, as there is a possibility that those were your last words with your parents.'

For some time I felt guilty, but then eventually I thought I had done the right thing—by giving them of the exact picture I would have just increased their tension and nothing else.

The phone started vibrating again. It was Anmol calling. He was my batchmate and worked in the front office. When I picked up the call, he sounded very depressed. He wanted to know if I was safe. 'Ankur, I got to know that you are still hiding and that you had an encounter with the terrorists as well. Is it true?'

Since he already knew, I simply said, 'Yes'.

'I am so worried, dude. Do not take any chances, somebody will definitely come to take you out,' he said, almost crying.

He sounded as if he was the one guiding every single person in uniform. I don't know why and how, but finally I was the one consoling him rather than the other way around, given that he had managed to get out of the hotel. I said, 'Don't worry, dude, we are very safe over here and I am sure before the morning I will be out of this place.'

'I am praying for you guys,' he said and hung up the phone.

Surender stared at me and asked, 'Why were you consoling him, it's supposed to be the other way, isn't it?'

'He was actually sounding more scared then me, he needed consoling more than I did, so I just gave it to him.' We both started laughing.

'How come they are all calling at the same time and asking after our safety? Is it a coincidence or are they all in touch with each other?' asked Surender.

Before I could answer him, I got a call from Ankush, another batchmate who was watching it all on TV. This call was more informative than any of the others. Ankush thoughtfully shared all the information he had. He told me about Chef Kanishq, who had lost his life while in the main kitchen. He also updated me about Micky and Shivendu—they were looking for a way out of the hotel. He then gave me all the latest news and updates. 'Ankur, try and come out of the hotel,' he finally said. 'The situation is now better outside and there isn't any trouble. It's only inside the hotel now,' he said.

I gave him my location since he was in touch with the outside world. I thought that if somebody came to rescue us, at least they would know the place and, most importantly, would not miss us. Otherwise it would be very difficult to locate us as we were hiding in a place which few people knew about. Ankush said, 'It's good that you have told me your location, now let me inform the right people and they will take you out.' He also appreciated the place that we were hiding in; he said, 'I wouldn't have thought about this place and I am sure it will be impossible for someone not from the hotel to find it.'

If nothing else, Ankush's statement gave me the satisfaction of feeling that even if the terrorists came this way they would not be able to figure out our location.

I heard another big bomb blast. I was sure this one was the most serious so far. It was so powerful that we felt as if it had happened right on top of us. The vibrations of the blast were so strong that they easily shook the temporary structure of our hiding place. The vibrations continued for the next five to seven minutes and we could do nothing but pray to God that the room did not collapse. For that span of time, we were completely silent and uncertain of our fate.

One of the banquet staff said, 'Sir, we are sitting on top of the linen room which is full of clothes. Even if one cloth catches fire for some reason, the entire room will be in flames, and evacuation will not even be an option for us.'

This simple statement took our breath away. Just some minutes ago we had been feeling secure and now we realized that we were sitting on top of a volcano which could erupt at any moment. But we did not have any option except to be optimistic, so the banquet guy was told to shut up.

Another call came and the mobile screen read Snigdha Ma'am. She was our training manager and we reported to her through the entire programme. She was one of the most practical ladies I had ever come across. She was very strict but fair. The statement that I heard the most about her was, 'She knows her stuff'. I was surprised to see her call at around four in the morning. I knew she would definitely ask about our safety, but I hoped that since she herself was calling up the call would be more productive.

'I hope you guys are safe?'

'Yes, miss, at least till now,' I replied.

'Don't worry, we all are there with you and will make sure you come out safe as well,' she said in a motherly tone. 'I know that you guys are hiding in the linen room and that is one of the safest places to hide in a situation like this.'

I understood that she had spoken with Ankush. She added, 'I have given the information to the right people. Do not even think of taking the risk of moving out all by yourself. Somebody will definitely come shortly.'

She also inquired about the others, though she had a better idea about them than I did. I was comforted to think that people were aware that we were hiding in the linen room and that they would come to take us out.

CHAPTER FIFTEEN

4:15 a.m.

Noises in the Dark

Till now we had been sitting upright, poised to start running if need be, but now the exhaustion of my twenty-hour day was catching up with me. It was not only mine but everyone's energy levels that were going down, and we were feeling very low. I leaned back on the linen and stretched my legs out on the clothes. Seeing this, Surender teased me, saying, 'We are not even sure if we will be able to see the morning and you are stretching your bloody legs?'

I replied, 'Dude, let me relax and then die. You never know—what if hell doesn't have a comfortable bed for me?'

We laughed and relaxed a bit. Surender said, 'Boy, do you think is this the right time to check on Vineet and Simon?"

'I think so,' I replied. I took out my phone and dialled Vineet's number and looked at Surender. He was suddenly looking very tense. The phone was about to ring when he snatched it and ended the call. I was not surprised.

'I think we should call after some time. It might still be very risky at this stage,' he said.

I was also having second thoughts, but realized that it had been more than an hour since we had all been together at the Chambers. I was sure that during this one hour they would have found a place to hide. I shared this thought with Surender as well. I think I was convincing enough and he agreed. He had my phone and he took it out and looked at the dialled numbers log screen and started staring at me. I didn't understand the reason for the pause and asked him, 'Now what?'

'Wait,' he replied.

He was clearly trying to concentrate on something else. I tried my level best to understand what was going on but I couldn't. Finally I asked him again, 'What happened, why you aren't calling up?'

'Hey, can you hear something?' he asked.

'No, but once you make a call I'll hear Vineet's voice,' I replied. 'Now would you mind not frowning and making the call?'

'No, seriously, I can hear something,' he insisted.

I wondered whether he was playing a prank. 'Dude, if by any chance you are playing a prank on me then it's a very bad idea,' I said. Surender was concentrating to such an extent that he didn't even bother answering me. That's when I got scared and asked, 'What is it, what kind of sound?'

'Somebody is moving in the linen room. Might be coming towards us,' he said, making hand gestures at all of us, signalling us to make no noise.

Everyone started hiding themselves under the clothes again. We wanted to conceal all signs of life in the room. Suddenly, we heard a sound. In a couple of minutes, the noise was identified itself as that of footsteps.

'Someone is coming in,' I said. There was no response from anyone as we were just trying to figure out his movements. We could sense that the movement was very slow ,which meant that the person entering was very cautious. I asked Surender, 'What do you think?' He just gave me a blank look and did not respond. He was sweating a lot and looking very scared. The intruder was coming closer and we had no option but to hide ourselves as much as possible. We could hear him very close to us. And then he stepped on the first stair up to the room. We all burrowed further into the clothes. There wasn't any noise so we could hear the steps one after the other very easily. Surender and I joined hands and held each other very firmly. I think he wanted to tell me that if even one bullet came out of the terrorist's gun, we would get up and kill the son of a bitch. I was silently assuring him of the same.

Though our chances of survival seemed slim, I still did not lose hope. The person climbed up to the room and stood right in the middle, perhaps trying to look around. I could not see him as I was covered with clothes and I think this was the case with everyone else as well. The terrorist was probably trying to look for us; I could hear his movements in the room. I heard somebody whispering, 'Where are you guys?' We could see the intruder's shining black oxford shoes. I shook Surender's hand and we peeped out of the clothes. It was one of the banquet staff. He had been following us when we were at the Chambers but was lost in the middle. I took a deep breath and relaxed. This was the third time I had felt I might not be there the next moment.

'Where were you?' I asked the guy.

'I was with you when we all arrived at the linen room below,' he replied. 'But then after some time you all disappeared and I got lost between the aisles of linen. Thank God, I heard someone climbing up and a couple of minutes ago I found this staircase,' he added.

'Why didn't you shout at that time? We would have stopped for you,' said another staff member.

'I could not see anything, and I was too scared to speak,' he replied.

'You took more than an hour to find the staircase?' asked Surender.

'I couldn't stand as it was completely dark. I would have bumped into something. So I had to crawl like a snake. Besides, it is my first time in the linen room, and that too without lights.'

'Do you realize how much you scared all of us?' commented other of the banquet staff before adding, 'Come join me and let's hide together.'

The newcomer went to the other side and hid behind the single bed and we, sitting on the other side, didn't know whether to laugh at each other or weep with relief.

We were just remembering Vineet and the others when Vineet called on Surender's cell. He picked up the phone, said hello and nodded and smiled to inform me that everything was well. I could not understand the conversation between them as he was whispering. After their conversation was over I asked Surender about them.

'Before the attacks, Vineet was standing on the other side near the Chambers back area and Simon was right in the middle of the queue. After the first gunshot everyone ran like headless chickens and Vineet ran towards the staircase next to the Chambers entrance that takes one towards the engineering department and ends at the rear of the laundry. While running he met Chef Mathur and took him and a few others along. They all went inside the laundry and Vineet tried closing the massive metal fire door.'

'Isn't the door very heavy? How could he do it all by himself?' someone asked.

'Vineet climbed up the rope and pulled it down and closed it,' Surender replied.

'Where were the others?' I asked.

'When Vineet turned around, he could not see even a single person. Everyone was hiding,' he replied.

'How rude!' commented one of the banquet staff.

'Since the entire area was dark he thought of climbing up the water pipeline, thinking that even if the terrorists entered they would not see him that high. So he went and sat on top of the pipeline. But then he looked down and realized that if he lost his balance he would be risking his life. He finally came down and tried to contact others from his group. He found that they all were hiding upstairs in a small washroom. So he also went and joined them.' He added, 'I am talking about twelve to fourteen people in a small washroom.'

One of the banquet staff commented, 'This group must also include some of the people who were habitues of grand bungalows, big offices and luxurious lifestyles. But now they are all hiding in a small washroom where they cannot even stand properly!'

I heard some noise coming from the outside and I mentioned this to Surender and the others. They all started smiling, looking at the boy who had entered last—our past experience with outside noises had not been that great. But I could indeed hear some noise. After a couple of minutes some of the others agreed with me, but we could not make out what the noise was.

'It might be one of the terrorists getting arrested,' said Surender hopefully.

'There's no noise, it's all in your mind,' someone else said.

Another guy took out his phone and read a message from his friend and said, 'It is the lockers getting evacuated.'

This seemed the best explanation for the noise. The guy behind me said, 'Let's go from here and evacuate with the people from the lockers.'

I was very confused—should we go or not? I really wanted to take the risk and leave this time, but my past experience of evacuation a few hours ago stopped me. I looked at Surender and his expression told the same story—even he was not sure about taking such a step. I worked up the courage to ask him, 'Do you want to take a chance?'

Surender looked at the stains of blood on his shirt and said, 'These stains are not of my blood and by no means did I want that to happen. Let's stay for some more time. Since you have informed people outside the hotel, somebody will definitely come to get us out.'

There was silence again. Nobody had the balls to say that he wanted to go out and take the risk. We could feel the weight of the situation. But one thing was for sure: knowing that other people were being evacuated from the lockers—but not us—increased our feeling of insecurity.

CHAPTER SIXTEEN

4:40 a.m.

Soul Shivers

Sitting in a small room of which half of the employees of the hotel were not even aware made us feel far away from the outside world. One operations management trainee, one supervisor and five or six daily staff—who would think of saving us and putting his own life in jeopardy? I started to question our decision to move to this room. Perhaps we should have chosen a better place to hide. Here we were sitting in this room which was entirely secluded from the rest of the world. Even if security were to take out people, we would be the last ones to be evacuated. I shared this thought with Surender, but his reply made me feel comfortable and easy. He said, 'This might be the last place that security visits; similarly, this might be the last place for the terrorists as well.'

I got another call from Ankush. Seeing his name flash on the screen, I figured that he must definitely have some good news to share.

'Hey! How are you doing?' he asked. 'I have good news to share with you.'

I was obviously happy to hear this and was curious to know more. I thought a rescue team would be coming to us in order to get us out of the hotel.

'Micky and Shivendu are out of the hotel. Isn't that great?' Ankush said.

It feels awful when you hear bad things about friends, but this news created a blend of emotions for me. For all of us, really. I was really happy to hear that they were out of the hotel and safe, but I was also feeling very insecure to know that everyone other than me was managing to get out.

'But how did it happen? They were right in one the hot spots of the hotel. Surely it was not easy for them to get out so early?' I said to Ankush.

'No clue as of now, my friend, but I got the information and thought of updating you,' he replied. 'I didn't want to scare you, but the attacks are now becoming really big and I am sure this is not a small thing,' he said.

'What do you mean, exactly?' I asked. '

All the news channels including the international channels are right up there and covering each byte of it,' he replied.

'Hey! Be honest. Do you think the situation will be under control soon?' I asked.

'I think so. The news channels say that NSG commandos have been called from the whole country and they will be on a special operation to kill the terrorists.' Before ending the call, Ankush also assured me that he had informed the security people through Ms Snigdha and a couple of others who could help. 'There will be some people coming very soon to get you out. Till then, do not move from your hiding place,' he said.

I hung up and called Micky. I wanted to know about their escape and congratulate him.

'Hey, bro, we have just come out of the hotel. What is the scene with you?' he said. I could hear the sense of freedom in his voice, though he was still very worried about others in the hotel.

'I am glad to hear about your escape, but how did you manage it? Did someone come to get you out or was it one of you who took the decision to evacuate?'

'We had the advantage of being near the road, and that too in the corner. We broke the glass pane of the window and called the fire brigade, who brought a ladder, with the help of which we managed to come out of the hotel.'

'That was brave. But what's the plan from now onwards?' I asked.

'Now we are waiting for the buses to take us to Wellington Mews.'

I informed him about our location as well and he assured me that he would tell someone in security to get us out. He also gave us another bit of good news. Ankita, who had been hiding somewhere in the lockers area, was also out of the hotel now. In order to pump in some positive energy, he also said that if the lockers had been evacuated we would certainly be next.

The news was really positive, but it also left us with lots of fear. I gave the information to Surender, and though I put a positive spin on it, I could see his stress levels increasing. 'When the entire world is out of the hotel, why are we waiting for the terrorists to come and remove us from the world?' he asked in frustration.

I tried to calm him down, saying, 'Don't worry, people are aware that we are hiding in here.'

'I am not a kid, don't fool me or yourself. The nineteenth floor has been evacuated. Why do you think a security guy would come just for one supervisor, one yet-to-be-confirmed employee and a bunch of idiots working on a per-day basis?' he asked in an aggressive tone.

I tried to console him again. The debate carried on and, if nothing else, kept us busy and we were able to successfully kill time.

Something was bothering me, though. I thought that we were communicating our location of hiding a little too freely. There was a possibility that the information would leak to the terrorists. We could not even trust our shadows. I remembered speculating that the shootout at the Chambers happened during the evacuation due to the leaking of information on the evacuation plan. This could happen to us as well. I could not control my thoughts and I wondered what would happen if I became a hostage the next moment. I was about to share this thought with Surender, but then I stopped myself, thinking that he was not feeling very positive to start with. If I even mentioned the word hostage, it would just worsen the entire situation.

'Ankur, what are you thinking? Is there something wrong?' Surender asked me curiously.

'No, not at all,' I said. 'Do you feel there is?'

'No, but you are looking very tense. If there is something wrong you can tell me,' he said.

'How can you say that I am looking tense? It's all dark in here. I can't even see your face and here you are telling me that my face expresses tension?' I said jokingly, trying to make the atmosphere a little lighter.

It worked, and couple of the banquet staff started laughing.

'I feel rather positive and I think everything will be all right as soon as dawn breaks,' I said.

'How can you say that? Did someone tell you so?' Surender asked.

I was not sure why, but I was somehow sure that something would happen in the morning and everything would be all right. I just felt this from within. Mentioning this at that point of time was not appropriate ,so I just said that my information was through a reliable source and was definitely true. I did not like making up a fake story about a reliable source, but I could see that it was boosting everyone's morale and, indirectly, mine as well.

I suddenly realized, as I was looking at the guy behind the single bed, that I could not see him moving at all. Watching him closely, I saw to my surprise that he was sleeping. I couldn't believe it and so I told the others to wake him up. They tried, but he was in a deep sleep. I was wondering what we would do if the terrorists came while he was sleeping and I could not think of anything beyond that.

'Sir, he is in a different world altogether, he will not get up,' one of the guys said.

'But isn't he scared of an attack? How can he even think of sleeping?' asked Surender.

'Sir, he does not have any relatives in this world. He doesn't care much about himself and he doesn't have to answer to anyone,' one of the guys said.

We were shocked to hear that, and of course now we had a little more sympathy towards him.

It is true what they say: whenever you are in a bad situation, just look around and you will find yourself in a better state than others. I now looked at the guy from a different angle as he slept. There was shouting and terror all around, and here the guy was relishing his sleep without any tension!

For a couple of minutes even I forgot that I was sitting on a volcano as I watched him enjoying the present moment.

CHAPTER SEVENTEEN

5:20 a.m.

Virgin's Talks

'Dude, it's past fucking five,' Surender said in a bantering but clearly frustrated tone.

'What's wrong with you? Even I can see that,' I replied.

'I know you can. Why is no one coming to get us out of this shit?' he said.

'Don't behave like a spoilt kid in a school bus asking "When is my stop going to come?"' I snapped.

'I am so irritated. I just want to go out of here,' Surender whined like a child.

'Do we have an option?' I asked, at which he had to keep quiet.

We all were irritated, but not enough to risk our lives. I gave Surender the cold shoulder as I didn't know how to react to his outburst. I looked away, resting my head on my arms. He gave me a pat on my back and said, 'Let's just run out of here!'

I looked at him for a second, shocked. The others also stared at him, everyone's jaws dropping. Nobody had the guts to say anything after that. There was complete silence for the next minute. The atmosphere became very serious all over again and everyone looked at each other, expecting someone to comment.

My mind was running really fast. Most of my thoughts were unproductive and weird, but it was as if my mind was not under my control. I turned towards Surender and was about to say something when he said, very innocently, 'I don't want to die a virgin.'

For the next couple of seconds I tried to convince myself that he had actually said that. After that, neither of us could control our laughter. It was a real challenge to laugh without making noise! '

Are you serious? Did you really just say that?' I asked.

We were still laughing when Surender added, 'It's not only that,' and his tone became more serious. 'I have lots of dreams which I want to fulfil before I die.' The conversation took a serious turn.

'I think I have not even started dreaming maturely. Fulfilling them is way ahead.'

That's when we started discussing our dreams and goals. It was ironic, discussing our future dreams while we were not even sure that would we be able to get out of this place alive.

'I was always interested in becoming an actor. I have done a lot of theatre, and even the lead role in a couple of documentaries,' I told Surender. 'I love playing instruments as well and I wanted to pursue mass communication as a career option,' I said, telling him about my past.

'I am impressed,' said Surender. 'I heard that you were into public speaking as well.'

'Yes, I was, but never took it very seriously, though I loved it,' I replied.

'What are you doing in this hotel?' Surender asked sarcastically. 'Why don't you join somewhere else and do what suits you more?'

'It was only by chance that I ended up in hotel management,' I explained.

'And destiny brought you to the Taj Mahal in Mumbai to experience this day,' commented Surender.

'There is a twist to that as well,' I started explaining. 'I was supposed to go the new Taj property opening in Trivandrum and I hate South Indian food. Just a couple of days before I was supposed to go, I was told that the property opening was delayed and my new destination was Taj Mahal, Mumbai.'

Surender was surprised to hear all this and after asking me another couple of questions he started telling me about himself. He told me about his entire journey, all the sacrifices that he made during his tenure at the Taj, and so on. 'Why is the life so complicated, why can't it just be smooth and easy?' he asked.

Our conversation became rather philosophical and we ended up doing a ritualistic 'guy' thing: we started comparing life with a girl who always ditches and hurts you just when you start expecting something from her.

The rest of the area was silent while we were busy chatting. Suddenly, the intercom telephone started ringing. During the general flow of operations one tends to miss these calls due to the low tone, but now it seemed very loud because of the silence in the room.

'Oh shit, what is that?' Surender asked.

'The linen room phone,' I answered.

'That I know, but who the hell would be calling up the linen room at this point of time?' he asked.

'Is it possible that the evacuation team might be calling us, in order to confirm whether we are here or not?' I said.

'But that would mean that if we don't pick up the call, they will never come to get us out of here,' he said.

'It might be the terrorists as well, using this phone like a dangling carrot,' one of the banquet guys said.

'But even if we were to answer, who will go down?' asked another.

'Taking it positively would mean that we have to answer this call and let them know of our existence. The phone has been ringing forever!' I said. 'But who will go down and take the call?'

Surender stood up, Bollywood-style, and was ready to go. I didn't feel comfortable and stopped him. I think he also was not sure whether to take this step or not, so he sat down again with the same level of tension. 'Just have patience, guys, and believe in God,' said Surender. He was looking very serious.

Though it was our decision to not pick up the call, I wondered if we had made the right choice. I hope I have not missed the call of my life, I said to myself. Surender mentioned calling Vineet and checking if something was happening at their end. 'Not a bad idea,' I said, and Surender dialled Vineet's number.

It turned out there was nothing new; they gave us the same news as before. The position over there was even worse than ours. Here we were able to sit, and could even stretch our legs easily, whereas over there they could not even stand properly.

Vineet said it was so hot and humid that they were literally drenched in sweat. While Vineet and Surender talked, we heard the noise of a couple of gunshots. I told Surender to hang up as the terrorists might hear his voice. I think Vineet also heard this and told Surender to end the call and be alert.

'I think the noise of the gunshots is coming from the Chambers,' said Surender.

As he said this, I remembered that Simon and some others were hiding in the Chambers. 'Will they be safe over there?' I asked Surender.

'I am sure they would have taken all possible precautionary measures over there. Still, I am afraid,' he said. 'The terrorists may take them hostage.'

We couldn't do much but pray for them, and for ourselves.

CHAPTER EIGHTEEN

6:00 a.m.

Phone Calls

We had been lying in the same place for quite some time now. We were obviously tired and almost broken. Suddenly, Surender started talking about the beginning of the incident. 'I could have easily left in the beginning,' said Surender.

'Then why didn't you leave?' asked one of the guys.

'How was I supposed to know that what started as a couple of gunshots could turn into this massacre?' he replied. 'I just wanted to save somebody's life.'

The banquet casuals were getting interested in the discussion and started showing interest. Looking at them listening, I was sure that Surender would make up stories from nowhere. 'Look at these torn pants, what do you think caused this?' he asked.

They were so engaged that they almost forgot about the incident and started throwing some wild guesses around. 'Was it because of a nail that went through it while you were running?' one of them asked.

'No, it is from the bullet which came so close that my pants got torn and by the grace of God I didn't even get a scratch,' he said.

Oh God, this was so untrue that I thought these guys might insult him by laughing. To my surprise, they all were convinced by the story! I could not believe that these people were taking it seriously. Till date, I don't know if it was true or not, but I must applaud Surender for making the entire thing sound so truthful and exciting, especially in a situation like the one we were in. The cherry on the cake was a comment that one of the guys made: 'It would have been like that scene in *MI-2*'. I didn't know how to react.

Though all this talk was keeping us busy, sitting in one small, dark and warm room, in the same position, was sickening. It had been many hours, after all. We felt like prisoners. Unfortunately, we had no option other than to wait and wait and wait. I leaned back a little and pushed the pile of linen with my back to stretch my legs. I wanted to relax a bit.

My eyelids were heavy. But I could not close them even for a couple of minutes. Every time I tried to nod off, I got the feeling that the terrorists were coming for us.

Surender's phone rang. 'Just be quiet, make no noise and don't say anything,' he said. I thought this might be because he didn't want any disturbance during an important call. 'Hey, Mom!' he said as he answered the phone. I was surprised to see his expression, which was normal, as though there wasn't anything wrong. 'I am absolutely fine, Mom. Hope you are also doing well. And yeah, don't worry at all, Mom, everything is going to be under control very soon.' He spoke in a normal voice, which seemed very loud in that situation. I signalled to him twice to lower his volume, but he just ignored me. 'I am with a lot of other friends and security has surrounded us from all sides with really big guns in their hands,' I heard him say, and that's when I realized why he was trying to act so normal. For the next five minutes he just listened to whatever his mother said. Before ending the call he mentioned that he'd be back home soon.

I didn't say anything, but Surender started to justify himself. 'Ankur, I didn't have any other option but to lie.'

'It's okay,' I replied. 'I can understand.'

I too felt bad that I had lied to my own parents. I thought about what would happen if I got killed, about how my parents would feel. This thought brought tears to my eyes.

It was quite some time later that I received a call from someone updating me about the status outside. I thought of calling other batchmates and took out my phone. To my surprise, the phone was switched off. I fiddled with it, but there wasn't any battery life left and it remained switched off. 'I want a phone,' I said, looking at everyone.

'What happened to yours?' asked Surender.

'It has run out of battery and I am sure people will be trying to contact me,' I replied. Surender was about to take out his phone's battery, but I realized that he was in constant touch with Vineet and others. I didn't want to disable his phone. I looked towards a casual and asked for his phone. 'Can I borrow your phone till we get out?' I asked him.

'Ah...I...my phone is, I think, not working properly... Do you still want it?' he replied. I was surprised to see that he was worried about giving me his phone, thinking I would not return it to him. I was the only person in touch with the outside world, so I made him an offer. 'I take your phone and you take mine… Mind you, mine is almost four times the price of your phone and you don't return it if I don't return yours,' I said. I could not believe that he was still thinking this offer over. I had to negotiate further by offering him some money as security, thinking that money would come again but not life.

Listening to our conversation, another casual got up and told this guy, 'What's wrong with you, dude? He's the one who's trying hard to get us out and you can't even offer your phone?'

I think this reprimand worked and the guy was kind enough to exchange phones and did not take the security money. Finally, his phone was in my hands and I opened both the machines up to exchange SIM cards. My hands were shivering in anticipation of news from the outside world, and due to this I dropped my SIM card somewhere in the bunch of linen. One bit of bad luck after another! Surender started searching for the SIM card. He found it really quickly, but those few seconds were tough. I got the feeling that something would go really wrong and the loss of the card was an omen. I assembled both phones with interchanged SIM cards and handed my phone over.

As I switched the phone on, the screen lit up with an incoming call from Sumit, another friend from Delhi who worked at another Taj property. 'Hey, bro, are you still in the hotel or did you manage to escape?' he asked in a very excited tone.

'I am still stuck, but what's the reason for your excitement?' I asked. 'Nothing, bro, but let me tell you, you have become bloody famous. Everyone's talking about you,' he replied.

I didn't know whether to be pleased about being famous or sad for being in the hotel. I shared the thought of becoming famous with Surender and, as expected, he also became excited about it. However, he said something which took my breath away. 'Will I still be famous if I don't walk out myself but am carried out on four shoulders?' Nobody had a word to say after that.

Just to lighten the mood, I asked Surender, 'What do you want to do once you are out of here?'

His response was very practical: 'Rest.'

He asked me the same question. I was quite predictable in my answer. 'I want to go back home and hug my mom and my dad and catch up with all my friends and family. And I never want to come back here again.'

Saying this, I suddenly realized how much the value of all the people I knew had increased with my loneliness in the past hours. Earlier they were just friends and family, but now they felt like much more than that.

'What do you mean, you don't want to come back? Are you planning o quit?' Surender asked.

'No, I want to transfer to Delhi instead,' I replied.

'You think you will be able to get it easily?'

'I need it—and they'd better give it to me,' I replied with confidence, as if it was all in my hands.

After a few minutes, I called up Ritika to get some news. 'How are you doing?' came Ritika's voice from the other end.

'I am having a great time. Sitting by the poolside and soaking up the sun, having a glass of champagne. I hope you are not feeling jealous?' I commented sarcastically, which silenced her. 'I am fine, just waiting to get out of this shit,' I said finally.

She told me that almost everyone from the hotel was out now. 'The two major areas of the Chambers and the basement laundry and linen room are yet to be evacuated,' she said.

'Should I take it as good news that people are getting out or bad news that I am still not out of the hotel?' I asked.

'No, yaar, I just want you to be aware of the situation and get out as soon as possible,' she said. She also told me about Bhavna, the management trainee working at the Golden Dragon. She was stuck in the Chambers when one of the guests was hit on the knee by a bullet. He had blood flowing from his leg like water. 'Bhavna and other people over there are very scared,' said Ritika. What else could one be when someone was bleeding right in front of their eyes?

'Why don't they provide some kind of first aid?' I asked.

'Of course they have given first aid, but the blood is refusing to stop flowing,' Ritika said. 'The condition is really bad and it is now an emergency.'

I felt very bad for them and thanked the Almighty that I was in a much better state, sitting in the linen room. I shared the information with Surender and he echoed my feelings. He too had a friend stuck in the Chambers and tried calling him to know about the situation. The friend didn't pick up the call but they communicated through text messages. He said that it was all dark and there was not even a single ray of light. They had closed the doors and laid chairs and tables in front of the doors so that nobody could open them. However, they could hear the terrorists' footsteps and the sound of gunshots and other activities just on the other side of the door.

Just then, I got a call from an unknown number. The number seemed familiar but I had second thoughts about answering the call, recollecting what the chef in Wasabi had said about not answering any unknown numbers, and even if we did, to take care not to say anything that leaked out important information. It was a do-or-die situation, so I went ahead and picked up the call.

A very confident and assured voice came from the other end, saying, 'Ankur, we are aware about your location and rest assured that somebody will definitely come to rescue you.' It was Saransh, my official mentor during my training. 'Kindly do not take any wrong decision or step that might land you in trouble.'

I could not say anything beyond 'Certainly, sir.'

This call was very comforting. However, as always, this positive feeling was short-lived as Surender said, 'Ankur, is there a possibility that the terrorists might get to know we are hiding in the linen room and make us hostages over here?'

'Are you trying to scare me?' I asked.

'No, it's just that everyone's been advertising our location,' he replied.

'Dude, everyone's just trying their level best to advertise it in order to get us out of this shit. They are doing it for our own good.' I tried to make him think positive even though somewhere in the back of my own mind there was a niggling doubt that it was not helping much.

There was silence for a couple of minutes. Finally, Surender said, 'Brother, I know they are not doing this intentionally, but wasn't this the same situation that led to the attacks at the Chambers? Don't you think that they came to know about the evacuation and that was the reason the attacks were timed just right?'

I stayed silent. Deep in my heart, I was carrying the same fear. I was also worried that if the terrorists came instead of the security people, we wouldn't even be able to run away.

Soon, I got a call from a friend from Bangalore. She was also friends with Bhavna, the girl hiding at the Chambers. 'Hey, Ankur, I hope you are safe?' she asked.

I had no option but to say yes.

'I got to know about you through Bhavna, are you aware about her situation?' my friend asked.

'Oh yes, I heard about it. I believe she is not in a very good state and there's someone bleeding in the same room,' I replied.

'Yeah, and she is very scared. I am really worried for you guys.'

'I hope Bhavna is able to cope with it. Please be in constant touch with her. But don't worry about us, we'll be fine and out soon,' I replied and hung up. I wasn't in a mood to speak to anyone any more as there were already loads of things going through my mind. I was steadily losing hope.

'Surender, do you think it would be a good decision to make a move all by ourselves?' I said. 'It's just about a hundred metres.'

He thought a bit and said, 'We have already waited for so long, and if people are telling us not to take any step, and that they will come any time now, then why take the risk?'

I knew that if I wanted I could have convinced them all to move, but even I wasn't sure about this step. We could do nothing wait, hopefully for only a little longer.

CHAPTER NINETEEN

7:30 a.m.

Rescue Operations

We were just sitting and waiting and could not see any ray of hope. It seemed that every effort was going down the drain. We were all just hopping here and there and changing positions. It was like a game of cat and mouse and we, undoubtedly, represented the mouse running for its life.

My whole body was aching as I had been awake for almost twenty-four hours and my last sleep had not been particularly relaxing. By now, our hiding place seemed very uncomfortable and cramped. I was thirsty, with a bone-dry throat after speaking to one and all, and we had not even a single drop of water. Problems seem bigger when you can't see the solutions. It was a great lesson that I learnt for life.

A loud noise came from somewhere far. I heard somebody shouting 'Chef!' I did not react as I thought it was just my perception and maybe my hopeful mind was playing tricks on me. I decided to check with Surender. 'Hey, did you hear someone shouting?' I asked.

'No dude, nothing. Why, did you hear someone?' he replied.

He was so confident while saying no that for a moment even I doubted myself. But after a couple of seconds, I heard the same voice again. This time I was sure that there was someone around. It was either the terrorists or someone, finally, to save us. In either case, I could sense that something was about to happen.

I told everyone to maintain silence, to which they agreed. Though they were quiet, I was sure no one could hear the noise but me. They would have considered me crazy if the noise hadn't come again. When it did, everybody agreed that they had also heard someone shouting 'Chef!' Everyone started hiding under the clothes again. Finally there was some movement, but we were all praying that this movement was for the good.

When he heard the sound again, Surender looked at me. Everybody else was under the linen. I think they were counting on us to take some decision. We were not sure if it was security or the terrorists. Were they here to kill us or to save us?

Suddenly, Surender shouted, 'We are all here.'

This was the moment, and we were all frozen. We looked at each other with eyes wide open. I think Surender himself was not sure about what he had done. All we knew was that now was the moment which would decide our lives. After this, we would either leave the hotel and be free or leave this world.

Surender stood up and tried to peep down. 'Are you sure these guys are not the terrorists?' I asked.

'Oh, for sure, that is one of the security managers of our hotel.'

I took a deep breath of relief.

'Where are you guys?' came the voice of the security manager.

'We are here, sir, coming down,' I replied. With high hopes, one after another, we all started moving down the iron staircase.

Shamsher from security was standing right in front of us, like an angel with a gun in his hand. He was wearing a white T-shirt and dark blue trousers, looking very serious, and sweating. He looked like a real army commando.

'Come fast. Move!' he yelled. 'Where's the chef?' He seemed particularly worried about Chef Mathur.

'The others are all in the laundry,' I replied. 'Where exactly in the laundry?' Shamsher asked.

'They are up in the washroom of the laundry,' Surender said anxiously.

'Hey, why don't you come along with us to rescue the chef and the others and let these guys stay over here?' said Shamsher. 'We would take all of you, including the chef's team, out at one go.'

I thought that was a great decision, but a very tough one. Surender didn't even think twice and started moving with them. I was standing with some of these casuals just under the staircase. One of them was staring at me. I couldn't understand why at first, but then I realized that he was the one whose mobile was with me. I couldn't do much and I tried to ignore him.

Another guy said, 'Sir, don't you think we should have come out by ourselves? It does not seem as risky as we thought.'

I also thought the same, but before I could comment someone else said, 'Yeah, as it is there is only one person who has come to save us.' He said this as though as he had been expecting a whole battalion to rescue him. I wanted to tell him that even the one person who came did not do so for us but for Chef Mathur, but I didn't want him to feel bad.

'Come on, let's go,' I heard Shamser shouting from the other side of the room. A queue had formed to leave the place. We also joined it and I strategically placed myself fourth or fifth down, thinking I that would be safe from both sides. As we moved out of the room, I was shocked to see around ten or twelve commandos on either side, with guns in their hands and revenge on their faces. All of them were looking everywhere but at us. They were alert and poised to attack if the need arose.

We finally started the journey towards life and hope. We moved down the small lane towards the housekeeping office. Everything seemed to be under control, with commandos on both sides covering us. We were very near the lockers where we had to turn right towards the staff door. This time, I could see bloodstains on the walls and on the floor. I looked at Surender and I think he understood that I had been looking at those stains.

We reached the staff gate finally, but could hear gunshots there as well. The back lane was empty and sealed. 'Bend and run away from the hotel boundaries,' shouted the leader of the commandos. We followed his instructions and started running in the direction away from the hotel walls. I stopped some distance away and looked back. I could see Shamsher waving at us, making sure everyone was safe and out of the hotel.

I looked at the staff who had been hiding in the laundry—

they were all drenched in sweat. They were also running with us. For some reason I stopped somewhere in the middle of the road and turned around to have a look at the Taj. I thought of the first day when I had entered the hotel. I remembered how I stopped John in the middle of the road to stare at the property. Today brought a different pleasure altogether. Looking at the building, I could not believe that I was out of it and that I had survived. The most difficult part was to believe that it was all real and not just a bad dream. I took a deep breath. It was a moment that I can never forget—and whenever I cross that street, I am sure I will stop by again to stare at the property from the same angle.

I went to the side of the road and sat on the pavement. I remembered my parents and thanked the Almighty. I had tears in my eyes. I was experiencing a cocktail of emotions—feeling good for all those who survived, feeling bad for the ones who could not make it. I also thought about the people still stuck inside and prayed particularly for those who were still inside the Chambers.

It was early morning. The cold wind struck my face. I could not stop my tears. I felt as if somebody had blessed me with another life, a feeling of rebirth. I could not believe that I was alive.

Finally I got up, looked around and realized that I was in my uniform and had just come out of the Taj. People were staring at me. But why was I alone? To my surprise I could not see even one of the survivors who had come out of the hotel with me. They had all disappeared. I came to my senses and started moving. I took the phone from my pocket and realized that it was not mine. It was the phone I had exchanged with the casual back in the linen room. I could not see him around. I was standing right in the middle of the road in my grey pants and blue coat, with somebody else's phone in my hand, with none of my contact numbers so that I could call up someone. I started browsing through phone, thinking to call the guy so I could get to him and my own phone.

'Hey, sir,' came a voice from behind me. 'I was looking for you. I thought you had left.' It was the guy with my phone . 'Sir, your phone is very attractive and I could easily have run away with it,' he said, to which I responded with a blank face. I didn't think it was a good time for a joke.

'Can I have my phone back, if you have finished admiring it?' I snapped.

'Sure, sir. And thanks for saving our lives. If you had not been there, we could not have come out so soon, perhaps never,' he said in a very heavy voice.

It touched me and, after a long time, a small smile appeared on my face.

We exchanged phones and parted ways.

CHAPTER TWENTY

9:00 a.m.

What Next?

Now that I had was back to my senses, I could relish the feel of being outside the hotel and free. I started walking down the lane connecting to the main Colaba road. From that particular spot, my room was about two kilometres away. Walking home was not unusual for me. While walking I tried my luck with switching on the phone. I wanted to inform, if not everyone, at least my family that I was now safe and out of the hotel. While I was doing this, I saw Chef Mathur and Chef Ravi coming towards me from not very far off. They were both completely drenched as if they had been caught in heavy rain. Chef Ravi also had a phone in his hands and was looking very depressed. 'I hope you are alright?' asked Chef Mathur, in a very low tone, putting a hand on my shoulder.

'Yes, chef, I am fine. And you?' I asked. I knew he wasn't all right, but still he nodded.

'Can I use your phone?' he asked. 'My phone is switched off.'

'Of course, chef, you can take my phone, but the battery is

almost dead,' I replied. Chef Ravi was staring at me in a very strange way. Perhaps it was because I refused Chef Mathur. Seeing this I said, 'But I am sure it will still support at least one call.'

Chef Mathur took the phone and made a short call. He gave the phone back to me, saying, 'Thanks, Ankur, I made the call.'

I could feel that there was something really wrong as neither of them were behaving in the usual way. 'You're welcome, chef, but I hope everything is fine,' I said, looking at both of them. They were quiet, but they clearly wanted to say something. I could not understand what were they trying to hide from me. 'Chef, can I be of some help?' I asked, thinking this might work.

'No, nothing,' said Chef Ravi in a heavy voice. He was about to say something, but before he could speak, his eyes filled with tears.

I had no idea how to react. I was speechless. I gathered some courage to ask again, 'Chef…ah…what happened?'

They refused to speak up, but the tears were increasing as they looked at each other. I took Chef Mathur's hand in my hands and asked him again, 'Is everything all right?'

He finally said, 'I lost my chefs.'

All three of us were now in tears. I remembered the day when we first met Chef Mathur. What an amazing personality, I had thought. Since then my respect for him had just increased. I could not believe that I was looking at the same strong man in tears today. But I could definitely see the softer side of the strong man. I could see the love, care and affection towards his fellow chefs.

Though I had a fair idea what he was talking about, I still asked, 'Chef, who are you talking about?'

It was very difficult for him to even speak, but he took all the names, one after the other. My respect for him increased further.

They crossed to the other side of the road and I started walking towards my place. I took out my phone and thought of calling home before it ran out of battery again.

'Mom, I am out of the hotel and safe now,' I said to my mother.

She was very happy to hear that and I could feel the emotion in her voice. 'Now you are fine, now you come back home,' she said, and these words made me very emotional.

'Sure, Mom, I'll be back very soon,' I said. After putting the phone down, I was in tears again. I realized then just how much I loved her and how much they all loved me.

I was depressed about the whole thing. I wanted to go to my room and relax, but I also wanted to see the front of the Taj. The entire area around the Taj was sealed. I could not go through the inner lanes. I thought of taking the outer road and going the long way. I reached the corner of the road which had the Taj on one side and the Gateway of India on the other.

I took the long road and went towards the front of the hotel. I wondered several times why I was not going straight to my room and relaxing rather than roaming in front of the attacked hotel. I even stopped at one point and thought of turning back but the feeling of being connected to the hotel drove me on. The Taj was 'my' hotel and the attack on it was something that I could feel in my belly.

The whole road was now a restricted zone with innumerable officials standing on all sides. I could see a number of fire brigades queued up, back to back. I came from the side lane of the Taj and entered the lane adjacent to the sea. Loads of people were standing in a big group just next to the barrier gate.

I could see the sea shining bright and reflecting the sun. I could see the boats moored in the sea moving with the flow of water. I could see a group of pigeons flying in their usual circles near the Gateway. I could see the sun shining bright, spreading its rays on the Taj dome. Innocent nature was not aware of this unusual day.

I could see two or three cops firing from the top of the Gateway of India. The other side of the Gateway was filled with with reporters and cameramen with all their equipment. They were lying on the ground. God knows how long they had been there. The roads were drenched in water from the fire engines and were shining with the reflection of the sun.

I stood right in front of the the Taj and could not even blink. A young chap, maybe in his mid-twenties, was standing just next to me with his camera. He was so engrossed in his work that he didn't even realize that I was staring at him. He was clicking away with his camera, taking numerous shots from all possible angles. After a couple of minutes, he noticed me looking at him. He ignored me at first but then, I think, he realized that I was in the hotel's uniform. 'Are you from the hotel?' he asked, lowering his camera.

'Yes, I am,' I replied, nodding my head.

'Did you just come out of the hotel, in the last evacuation batch?' he asked curiously. I was surprised to hear this and wondered how he was aware of all the evacuation that was taking place. I replied in the affirmative. 'How was it inside?' he asked in the way a small kid would ask a question. Did he expect me to say that the experience had been amazing and out of this world? I gave him a weird look and he just stepped back as if I was about to hit him. 'I am so sorry. I should not have asked that kind of question,' he said. Before I could reply he added, 'I am so, so sorry, I can understand, you must be feeling bad.' He went a couple of steps away and started clicking again as if he had never stopped.

It took me a few minutes to pull myself together. I went up to the guy and said, 'Excuse me,' in a polite tone.

'I sincerely apologize, I didn't want you to feel bad,' he said as if he had committed some crime.

'Shut up and don't be sorry, I don't feel bad at all,' I said.

Hearing this, he gave me a small but genuine smile.

I asked him if he was working for some news channel or the print media. He said no and this didn't surprise me as the entire press was capturing the event from opposite the Gateway of India. This lone guy with his camera was in a very risky location. 'Then who are you and what kind of fun are you having clicking these photographs?' I asked.

'I am a freelance photographer and I live in Pune,' he replied. 'I was here to meet a friend and was supposed to leave a night ago, but the trains got cancelled.'

'Oh really? Why?' I asked, forgetting about the entire incident in relation to the outside world.

'Because something happened in Mumbai last evening,' he replied, stretching the words out in a very sarcastic tone.

I was embarrassed; I could not believe that I had forgotten about the incident due to which I had almost died.

'So you were here the entire night clicking pictures?' I asked.

I was expecting a frustrated reply but it was just the

opposite. He was very enthusiastic. 'I was lucky enough that coincidentally I was in Mumbai itself and my train got cancelled, otherwise nobody would have had let me in and I would have missed the opportunity to come back to Mumbai.' I thought that he must be the only one man on earth who was happy about being in Mumbai that evening. Then I realized that last night even I had teased John about being inside the hotel while he was not. This guy clearly carried huge amount of passion and just loved what he did.

After saying goodbye to Mr Photographer, I started walking back towards my room. On the way to my room was John's place. I thought of calling him up and letting him know that I was out of the hotel. He told me to wait outside his apartment as he wanted to meet me. I stopped there for a couple of minutes and saw John walking down the stairs in his usual attire: chequered pants, his favourite blue T-shirt and a red cap. He came running towards me and screamed, 'Ankur, my friend, you are alive!'

'Yes, my Johnny, I am,' I said, and we hugged each other.

Oh, it felt so good! I could not believe that I was out of the Taj and, most importantly, alive.

'Come, Ankur, let's go and have a look at the Taj dome,' said John.

'No, bro, I just came out of that shit. I want to go home and relax,' I said.

'You can always go home and relax, but you can't see the Taj like this always. I think we should go there and have a another look,' he said in a very serious tone. I agreed and we went back to the Taj.

While on the way, we started sharing stories. He told me

about his experience outside the hotel and I told him of my encounters in the hotel and how we finally managed to escape. While we were chitchatting on the way, we met two of our colleagues from the hotel. 'Good morning, Mr Bhupinder, how are you doing?' asked John.

Mr Bhupinder was one of the oldest employees of the hotel and was always in the banquet lobby. He had a specific place to stand and oversee everything in the hotel. 'I am fine, how are you guys? I heard you were stuck in the hotel,' he said, looking at me.

'Yes, sir, I was.' I gave him a small glimpse of the whole thing.

I am sure even John was curious to know what Mr Bhupinder was doing over here as we remembered that he had left early last evening. When we asked him this, to our shock we found that he had not even been aware of the entire scenario in Mumbai. 'I went home, had dinner and went to sleep early. I got up for my morning shift, got ready and came straight to work. I didn't even get a chance to know about what was going on,' he said.

'So, when did you get to know about the whole incident?' I asked.

'When I reached in the morning for my usual morning shift, I saw the roads sealed around the Taj, and that's when I got to know.'

We had no idea how to respond to this. All we knew was that we couldn't afford to ask any more questions. I thought that there was something definitely wrong either with the world or with me. In the last hour, I had met three guys. The first was a passionate photographer, who was running against life to follow his passion. The second was John, who wanted to run towards the place from which people were desperate to escape, and then there was Mr Bhupinder, sleeping through this momentous night and coming to work thinking this was just another day, while the entire world watched the Taj on their TV sets.

We moved forward and parked ourselves as close to the police barriers as we could. We stood in front of the hotel and stared at the flames coming out of the dome. We could not even blink, we were so enthralled.

Suddenly there was a blast on the sixth floor, very close to the dome, and it was a heavy one. The glass of the windows broke and we could see the pieces falling on the ground. The fire expanded and clouds of black smoke started coming out from the window. Firemen stood under the dome and started spraying water with great pressure at the window, but unfortunately it was of no use. The fire refused to stop, and the smoke increased. At one point, the fire was so high that we did not think the dome would survive. We were just praying that the dome did not come down.

Soon, even the firemen understood that the water could not go so high. One of them signalled the other standing near the array of engines. One after another, fire engines came and parked in a queue. A shiny red van came in front and the men started assembling the folding ladder. A man with a hosepipe stood on the small carrier on the ladder and the ladder went up to the window effortlessly and parked itself at the window. This time, the water reached the fire and it was quenched, leaving behind a lot of smoke.

Chapter Twenty-one

11:00 a.m.

Back Home

I could not stand any more. I had now been awake for more than a full day. I think John was also losing interest. We finally thought of going back to our respective rooms. We started walking back and discussing what was going to happen next. We were both, obviously, clueless but still we could not stop speculating. It was as if we were the last two men on earth, walking down the street. For some time, we were both silent, but finally John asked, 'Ankur, do you think our management trainee programme will end because of what happened to the hotel?'

This did not seem the time for this line of thought, but it did make me wonder. I thought a bit and said, 'Maybe they will relocate us while this property gets refurbished.' The hope of a transfer back to Delhi came to my mind. We also talked over our estimates of damage that the Taj had suffered after this unfortunate incident. The conversation didn't feel good, as if we were the ones who were supposed to face the press after this. Our conversation took us the entire way and we reached

John's place. I was too tired to step up the stairs so I said sayonara and thanked him for the much-needed company and started moving ahead. He shouted from behind, 'Take care, bro. In case you need anything, feel free to call me,' and waved his hand.

As I reached the main road, about eighty metres from his place, I was almost limping from exhaustion. Last night I had sat in the same position with my legs folded for hours, due to which they were also paining like anything. I had been wearing a tight pair of formal oxford shoes for around twenty-four hours—I couldn't feel my toes any more. I also took off my jacket before it became too heavy to handle. I was craving food as there wasn't any dinner the previous night. Everything was making me uncomfortable.

Every single shop was shut this morning and I felt like a marooned man in a deserted place. Finally, I reached the road leading to my place. I could see that the entire road was empty and then, at a great distance, I could see a big group of people gathered together. I walked faster out of curiosity to know what was going on.

'Hey, are you from the Taj Hotel?' asked one of the kids standing nearby. I smiled at him. 'Were you also there when they were shooting everyone?' he added in his innocent voice. He was probably not even sure of what he was asking. I looked around and felt that I was becoming the centre of attraction for them as they could see my Taj uniform. As I got closer to the crowd, I got to know from one of the guys standing there that the nearby Nariman House was also under attack. The entire area was cordoned off and there were terrorists still inside the building. I could see commandos all around the place and on the rooftop of the neighbouring buildings. The noise of the gunshots and blasts was very prominent. On one side of Nariman House was the public, trying to peep inside the building to have a glimpse of the terrorists, and on the other side was the press with their cameras and other equipment.

I was trying to get a look at the place when the loud noise of a bomb exploding just on top of the building was heard. We could see the broken glass from the windows smashing on the ground and hitting the building across the street. The entire front row of the crowd stepped back and a panic was about to take over. Fortunately, the situation came under control in the blink of eye. However, it was kind of shocking for me that the crowd again took a step forward to watch. I realized that this was a very 'Mumbai' thing.

I was not feeling very comfortable standing in the crowd. The road was blocked on either side of Nariman House. I was sure that there was an alternative way home. I saw a group of cops, and thought of going to them to ask the way.

'Sir, could you tell me the way to Sasun Dak, as I will not be able to cross the road?' I was hoping that they might make an exception and allow me to cross the road.

'I am sorry, I will not be able to guide you as I am from Delhi,' the cop replied.

I smiled at him and said, 'Sir, even I am from Delhi.'

He responded with a smile. I knew it would work—he not only told me the exact route to my place but also said, 'Come along, I am also heading towards the same path.' So I followed him.

'Where exactly do you stay?' he asked.

'There is this small hotel called Happy Home, where one of the floors is for the dedicated use of Taj employees.'

Before I could say more, he interrupted. 'Oh yes, I know that place and some of the people who stay there.' I nodded and he added, 'I own a small tea stall nearby, come in case you want to grab some tea or coffee.'

I was in a dilemma. I was really hungry, but I also just wanted to go home. The matter was sorted as I remembered that I would not have much to eat at home. So I agreed to go along with him. I would go home after that. We reached his shop, but it was closed. He opened another door from the right side of the shop and asked me to follow him. From the look of it, it was a storeroom that he maintained. We went through a small white door and reached the shop. I looked all around for the things that could have been useful for me back home. All I could get from there was a couple of packets of milk, Maggi noodles and some biscuits. I remember him saying, 'Kindly drink the milk today itself as it might go bad after that.' I paid the bill and moved on.

While on the way, I could not resist my thirst, especially after looking at the packets of milk in my hands. I stood on the side of the road and opened one of them and in one go I finished it all. It was a bit embarrassing sucking milk from a plastic pouch on the roadside when half the city was under terrorist attack, but the feeling did not compare to the satisfaction that I felt after drinking the milk. It was just heavenly.

Finally, I reached my place. I went upstairs to my room. As I opened the lock of the door, I could not believe that what had happened in the last twenty-four hours was true. Here I was, safe and secure, as if nothing had gone wrong. I went inside, threw my coat on the couch, took off my tie and crashed on the bed. I didn't even have the stamina to change my clothes. I was lying down on the bed but I could not relax properly. My body was aching and I felt as if my head was about to burst. I heard someone passing by but I was not bothered and just wanted to have a good sleep. I think it was one of my roommates who came to see me but I just refused to get up. Once he realized how tired I was, he moved a couple of steps backwards, but then something made him come near me again.

'Hey, are you all right?' asked Jatin, my roommate, with curiosity.

'Yeah, I am fine but I am very tired,' I replied. This was the first time that I felt that one of my roommates was genuinely bothered about me.

'It must have been very scary, but I am sure you were very brave,' said Aarav. I think he wanted to be positive for my benefit.

We began talking and I realized that this was the first time my roommates and I had spent so much time in conversation.

'There must be so many people including your friends and your family who would have been calling you up,' Aarav said.

Jatin added, 'Sitting at home, we've got so many calls. I am sure you must have been harassed as you carry three phones on you.'

That's when I remembered that my phone's battery was dead and the other two were in the cupboard on silent mode. I got up and took the other phones out of the cupboard.

I used to carry three phones. One was a Vodafone Mumbai number, which I had bought when I landed in Mumbai. Another was my Delhi Airtel number, which I had used since my schooldays and which all my friends had, and the third was the Maharashtra Reliance phone, which I and another four friends had got for a special unlimited STD scheme.

I took the Delhi phone out and was shocked to see sixty-two missed calls. I didn't want to go through all the numbers and I was not even sure of how many numbers my phone could hold. However, I definitely wanted to have a glimpse of the known numbers to see if someone really important had called. The batteries in the other phones were also on the verge of dying so I took out all the chargers and connected them to their respective phones. While I was doing this, both Jatin and Aarav started laughing. I asked them why were they laughing, was I missing out on something? Both had the same sarcastic smile on their faces. Finally, they agreed to tell me as well.

Aarav said, 'Last night, as you also know, we were scared because of all the events taking place at our hotel. Besides, it is so near to our place that we could hear the noise of people shouting, as well as the bomb blasts themselves.' I could not understand what he was trying to say. 'Yesterday we were, like others, watching TV and were about to go to bed. Suddenly I could feel some vibrations, which made me very uncomfortable.'

'As in?' I asked.

'As in, he could not sense what it was but he could sense that there was something mysterious,' answered Jatin. 'We checked our room but we could not find anything. We did not feel comfortable but then it stopped.'

'But what was it?' I asked.

'We were curious as well, but it was mixed with fear,' said Aarav.

'Believe me, Ankur, the noise kept us busy for almost half an hour. It would start and then stop and so on,' explained Jatin.

'Did you find out what exactly it was?' I asked, wondering why they did not come to the point.

'It was your bloody phones which kept us occupied and worried!' said Jatin.

'Oh, shit!' I exclaimed.

'And the worst was that both your phones were in the locked cupboard and we could not do anything about it, but had to bear the noise for the rest of the night,' said Aarav.

We all laughed. I was a bit embarrassed but I didn't care much. I had not expected the chat to be so long, or that my roommates would become so friendly. They started telling me how it was being outside the hotel. Jatin mentioned that my phones were not the only reason for their disturbed sleep. They had been glued to the TV screen. They had also been in touch with people stuck in other Taj hotels.

'President Hotel was completely sealed when the attacks started,' said Jatin.

'Sealed! What exactly do you mean?' I asked.

'Nobody could come in and nobody could get out of the President Hotel. This included the guests who were not even staying there and were visiting just for a good meal,' he replied.

'Wasn't it a big thing to take responsibility for all the people inside? It could have been a bad decision if one of the guests was a terrorist,' I said.

'Were you also in touch with the people inside the Taj?' I asked.

'Yes, I had a word with Dhruv, who was sitting on the same

chair on which I usually do. I was supposed to relieve him tonight, a couple of hours after the incident began,' said Jatin.

'I believe he was in the lobby itself when the entire attack started,' I said.

'Yes, in fact, he was sitting in the duty manager's chair which is in the centre of the lobby,' said Aarav. 'He was sitting right in front of the glass wall when the terrorist came in and fired in the air and the entire wall came down just behind him.'

'Yes, I did hear the noise but I was not aware of what it was,' I said.

'It must have been really scary for a man stuck with a terrorist right in front of him and a broken glass wall behind him,' said Jatin.

'He was really lucky to be alive at that point of time,' I said.

'But I think the best part was that when I called him last night while he was hiding in the hotel. He was cool about the whole thing, as if nothing had happened,' said Jatin.

Although our chat was very interesting, they both understood that I was falling asleep. They got up and said I should rest for some time now and that I should let them know if I needed anything. I was surprised to see their care and affection towards me. This gave me a reason to be a bit happy.

I was still feeling very tired and I was starving. Cooking was the last thing on earth that I wanted to do. I opened my cupboard and took out some pinnis which Mom had packed for me when I was coming from Delhi and I made a glass of Tang for myself. I was feeling very depressed in the room; I took the rocking chair out and sat in the balcony for some fresh air. A bit of sunshine was falling on my balcony. I was

really missing home when my phone rang and—guess what—
it was my mom.

'Hi, beta! How are you?' she said.

'I am very good and I am having some warm pinnis after my
breakfast. How about you?' I had to lie about the warmness of
the pinnis and of course the breakfast, otherwise the next five
minutes would have been dedicated to a lecture over the phone.

'Everybody over here is asking about you. I have never
received so many calls in one night before,' she said. We
chatted for quite some time and I tried to convince her that
I was safe and well. Suddenly, I heard the big noise of a blast
which seemed to be very close.

'What was that?' Mom asked.

For a moment I was scared as I thought it was another blast,
this time very close to my place. I got up from my chair and
looked outside in all possible directions.

'Ankur, what was that?' Mom asked again.

'Nothing, Mom, it's the news channel on my TV set, they
are showing the Taj attacks, what else?' I said in a casual tone,
as if nothing was wrong. I shouted, 'Aarav, kindly turn the
volume down!' to convince Mom that Aarav was around and I
was watching TV with him.

I got the feeling that she saw through my lie. 'Speak properly
to your seniors, Aarav is elder to you,' she said, changing the
topic.

'Sorry, Mom, I know,' I said, feeling a bit uncomfortable
after that lie. 'Mom, I am really tired and I am going off to
sleep,' I said.

'All right, beta, but do take care of yourself,' she said and we
hung up.

I was not feeling very safe on the balcony, so I went inside and lay down on my bed. I saw that both my phones were charging and I added the one in my hand to the pile. I was about to slouch down on the bed when the phone started ringing again. I seemed to be getting calls from all over—some from people whom I didn't even know. In some cases, especially that of distant relatives, I had to pretend that I could recognize them from the brief intro that they provided to me. Initially, I felt good that there were people in the world who really cared about me, but after three or four calls I felt as if they were only calling me for the excitement of getting first-hand information over the phone. Some of the calls were really irritating, especially when all they wanted to know was whether I had seen the terrorists. The line of questioning was always along the same lines. First question (with deep emotion and every word stretched to the limit): 'Hey! How are you?' I wish I could said every time, 'I am alive, that's the reason for me picking up the phone.' Second question: 'Were you there?' This one made me laugh. 'Of course I was there, and that is the only reason you called me up.' Third question: 'Were you in the old hotel or the new one?' I had expected the media to clarify the internal layout of the hotel. However, I think they confused people even more. Fourth question: 'Did you see the terrorists?' I wish I could say, 'Yes, and I have also taken pictures with them and got an autograph with your name.' For God's sake, they were terrorists and not celebrities! These rapid-fire questions were pissing me off. And the worst part was that I could not even avoid them as it would be considered rude.

Keeping the phones away, I crashed. However, to my

surprise, I could not sleep. Whenever I closed my eyes, all I could see were people running here and there and bloodstains, and I felt scared and insecure even at home. I tried a few times, but I didn't have the courage to close my eyes. Every time my eyes were closed, the terror would increase. I felt as if someone would kill me if I closed my eyes. I sat up a couple of times and had drank some water. Then I lay down with my eyes wide open, thinking about the worst fourteen hours of my life. I don't know when I finally fell asleep.

I woke up in the evening. I was still very tired as I didn't sleep well. My back was aching. I decided to get up. I went to the washroom to freshen up. I came back and found my roommates watching TV and, inevitably, coverage of the attacks. I sat with them, thinking the incident was over. 'So how did it finally come to an end?' I asked.

'Not yet, dude, it seems as if it's neverending,' replied Aarav.

'In fact, it's getting worse,' added Jatin.

'What, is it not done yet? But why is it taking so long?' I asked.

'The terrorists are making fools of us by roaming inside the hotel and killing both time and people,' said Aarav.

'But why can't the armed forces get inside and kill them?' I asked.

'You think it is that easy?' said Jatin. I didn't like the way he said that.

'The army can't do that as the terrorists have taken some people as hostages,' explained Aarav, before he got busy with a phone call.

Jatin and I were still watching TV when the news broke about the family of Mr Kang, the general manager. He used to live, with his wife and three children, on the sixth floor of the hotel. The previous evening, Mr Kang had been sitting with Sabina Sehgal Saikia at Shamiana, after which he headed to Land's End and Sabina to her room on the sixth floor of the hotel. When he came back, the entire sixth floor was on fire. Sabina and Mr Kang's family were no more.

'That's sad, isn't it?' said Jatin, and I nodded.

Aarav came back into the room and said, 'I am feeling bored.' We didn't know how to react to that. It seemed inappropriate. 'What are we having for dinner?' Aarav asked. 'I don't think we have much stock left at home. We have to go out to the shop and get something to eat.'

'Shop? Yeah, right, let's go to the international store or why don't you call, they might do free home delivery,' Jatin said sarcastically, adding, 'You must be joking.'

'Will there be any shops open now?' I asked.

'Let's go out and see for ourselves,' proposed Aarav, to which I nodded, saying, 'I also have to get my phone recharged.' Jatin refused to come along. He remained glued to the TV screen.

I changed and got ready, then Aarav and I went out in search of food. I had never expected to have to search for food in a city like Mumbai. As expected, all the streets were completely empty. I could not see so much as a dog anywhere. We thought of moving towards the main road.

As we were about to reach the main road, I heard some vehicle, probably a truck, coming towards us. We reached the main road and saw a giant green army truck heading towards us. An army man was standing above the driver's cabin, holding a long gun mounted on top of the cabin. You could tell from his eyes that he was all set to shoot someone. We stopped right there, unable to take our eyes off those army trucks. 'Aarav, do you think we should reconsider our decision of going out? I don't mind sleeping another night without food,' I said, looking at him.

'Don't worry, bro; they won't harm you. They are for our security only,' he said coolly, as though this was an everyday occurence for him. I didn't want to talk further about it and we moved on. We took a right turn towards the market. Behind us was Nariman House, and we could see a lot of journalists and cameramen all around the place. The air was cool and the evening was dull with neither the brightness of sunlight nor the darkness of night. The entire place was very depressing and I felt as if I was in a war zone. Looking at all those cops with guns in their hands, I felt as if I was in Iraq or Afghanistan, where things like these are common and people like us search for food. We went ahead and tried to locate open shops but it was of no use. We gave up.

Aarav said, 'Let's go back home via a different route, we might end up finding something.' This sounded a brilliant idea and, on the way back, we found an old man boiling eggs at his stall. I couldn't have asked for more. We had some of those and I felt really satisfied. I remembered my dad as it was a Thursday, and Dad used to urge us to avoid non-vegetarian food on Thursdays. I am sure that day he would have given us liberty to eat eggs. We went a bit further and asked a couple of people standing on the roadside, but they couldn't help us find anything more. We had no option but to come back. We reached our place and informed Jatin of the situation. 'I was expecting that,' said Jatin, as if he was aware of what was happening outside. 'At last my food file will be helpful,' he said.

He maintained a file full of the menus of nearby restaurants which did home deliveries. We divided the menus equally and started calling them up with some hope, but somewhere we knew that this wasn't going to be much help. As expected, no one was working. After all, they were also human beings and living near the Taj.

I get a call on my Mumbai phone and when I saw that it was an unknown number, I thought it was one of the restaurants we had called. An unknown voice came from the other end. 'Hey! Am I talking to Ankur Chawla?' By his accent I judged that it was a NRI, maybe an American. But one thing was for sure, it was not a restaurant calling back.

'Yes, this is Ankur,' I replied.

'Hey, I am Shikhil, a freelance journalist. I got your number from your friend Micky.' Before I could ask him anything he said, 'I know you had a bad experience, but if you don't mind, can I talk to you further?'

For a moment I thought it was a prank arranged by one of my friends. I was always known for these things and I thought this call was an attempt to trap me. Still, given the sensitivity of the situation, I decided to take it seriously and said, 'Sure, please go ahead.'

'For this particular story, I am working for a Canadian news channel and I want you to speak live about your personal experience as a survivor,' he said.

I was not sure how to respond, but then I thought that everybody would be doing the same and there was no harm in helping him. My statement might earn this chap appreciation or, who knows, a promotion. I told him I was ready to do it on the condition that he wouldn't disclose any personal details other than my name. Since he didn't have much choice, he easily agreed. He told me that I would get a call from the studio directly in exactly thirty minutes and I would have to answer their questions.

After we hung up, I got a call from Jayant, a friend who was at Land's End. 'Hey, what's up?' said Jayant in his usual tone. We started discussing the entire incident and he shared his experiences at Land's End, the other Taj property in Bandra. However, this was not the reason for his call. 'Hey! Why don't you come over? As it is you are all by yourself in your room,' said Jayant. The offer was not bad as I didn't have much to do in my room, and besides, it would be better for me to be with him. However, I was scared to get out of my room and I was not in the right state of mind to travel from the south of Mumbai to Vile Parle.

'Thanks for the offer, but I would like to go to my home from here. I am dying to see my family,' I said, which I believe he understood. His mom came on the phone and even she tried to coax me to come to his place, but I just couldn't accept the offer. I thanked them and hung up.

Aarav and Jatin were standing in the kitchen exploring options for dinner, looking at what we already had and what could be made out of the available ingredients. I am sure it would have been an interesting conversation, but I hated cooking so I kept myself out of it. I sat for some time, playing games on my phone and then I got a call from an international number. I was sure it was the Canadian news channel.

I answered the call and I could hear a heavy voice on the other side. 'Hello, am I talking to Mr Ankur Chawla?' 'Yes, you are,' I said. 'You are going to be on air in fifteen seconds,' he said. 'All right,' I responded. It all sounded very unreal. After about ten seconds, I heard a voice, which I presume was the newsreader's. 'Here we have Ankur Chawla, an employee and survivor from the hotel under attack—Taj Mahal in Mumbai.' Now I was sure it wasn't a prank and I developed butterflies in my tummy. At the same time, I felt as if I was some kind of celebrity. 'Ankur, I am really sorry about the situation there, but how are you feeling now and how was it to be in such a traumatic situation?' I thought for a second and then said, 'It's all right. It was obviously terrifying and unfortunate to be in a situation like that.' He asked me several questions and some of them I refused to answer. I tried to be as politically correct and polite as possible—we never know when and how things can come back to haunt us. We had a conversation for a good five or seven minutes. Then he thanked me and expressed appreciation for all of the staff from the Taj.

After a few minutes, I also got a call from Shikhil, thanking me for the interview. After hanging up the phone, I was eager to tell Jatin and Aarav about it. However, I thought better of boasting about something like this. Besides, it might become a problem for me if everyone got to know.

I came back and saw Aarav in the kitchen trying to do something with the stuff we already had. I asked him what we were about to have and was told that Aarav was making some salad while Jatin was working on bread and butter. I also thought of involving myself so I took out my Tang jar and started making a drink for everyone. We all sat in the kitchen. We didn't have much conversation, but after all, this was the first time we were having dinner together.

After dinner, they both went to their room to watch TV

and I went to mine. I went to the balcony and stood there for some time to get some fresh air. I stood there, appreciating the atmosphere, the cool breeze and some peace. Finally, I felt a bit relaxed.

I went back into the room and sat before my laptop and started looking through the collection of pictures I had. My childhood, my family, my friends, all those trips with my near and dear ones, and so on. It felt good to cherish old memories. I was completely engrossed in my laptop when the phone calls started again, one after another. It was as though somebody had directed the callers to call me at the same time. I felt as if I was an employee at a call centre, responding to the same questions over and over again. I was too sleepy to deal with all the calls, so I switched off the lights and lay down on the bed while talking.

I don't remember when I my eyes closed, but I woke up in the morning to the wire of the phone charger coiled my body and the slideshow of family pictures on my laptop.

CHAPTER TWENTY-TWO

29 November

Aftermath

Finally, everything came to an end. The last couple of days were surely the most unusual time of my life. Bad, because I went through all that; good, as I survived it. I thought of all those who cared and prayed for me. And I remembered God from the bottom of my heart.

On the morning 29 November, the media was still showing the Taj Mahal Hotel and the other places hit by the terrorists. Images of those happy to be safe and reunited with their loved ones alternated with those grieving for lost family and friends.

John called me. 'Hey! Are you planning to go to the hotel?' he asked with excitement.

'Hotel?' I asked out of curiosity. 'Why do you want to go the hotel? Is all clear now? Are there any terrorists left inside?'

'Everyone's going and we should also go to assist. I think they need us over there,' he replied.

I was more than happy to join him as I really wanted to go and assist with things at the hotel. Besides, I was so bored sitting in my room for the past couple of days that I could not resist the chance to move out of its four walls. 'Will you wait for me or shall we meet directly at the hotel?' I asked him.

'Come to my place, we'll go together,' John said.

I immediately got ready and left my room. I could only see cops on the roads and the faces of people trying to see something from their balconies or windows. I picked John up from his place and we started walking towards the hotel.

'So, how is your vacation going?' he asked.

'Are you serious?' I couldn't believe he was asking such a weird question, but to keep the conversation going I said, 'I am only happy about one thing—the chance of a transfer back to Delhi.'

We both laughed.

When we finally reached the hotel, the lanes, as expected, were sealed from all sides. We could see loads of people standing around the Taj. We decided to try the corner lane which heads towards the Gateway of India with the Taj on the right hand side. To the left of the Gateway all I could see were journalists and cameramen from across the globe trying to cover every bit of it. We tried our best to get in, but the cops standing over there did not allow us through.

'Hey, guys, how are you doing?' came the voice of a lady from behind us. It was the head of the department of telephones.

'We are fine, miss. How about you?' I asked.

'I am good. Aren't they allowing us to go into the hotel?' she asked in a very commanding tone.

'No, madam,' John replied.

'Let me talk to these guys. You follow me,' she said as if she knew everyone over there. She was about to speak to the cops when suddenly Mr Kang appeared. His eyes were swollen and red, his hair was disorganized. His face looked as if he had not slept for the last three or four nights. We froze at the sight of him and nobody could speak a word. For the next few seconds we just stared at him. I wish I could salute that man, who had seen his family perish in the fire in front of his eyes and was still standing outside the hotel, trying to help in whatever way possible. Hats off to him.

'Let them in, they are from the hotel,' he said in a very fatherly tone.

We expressed our condolences and entered the hotel, moving towards the lobby entrance.

'Hey, Ankur, how are you?' said Shashank, the duty manager. We shook hands, happy to be alive even after being so close to death.

'So, you are alive?' I said.

'Yes, dude, and so are you!' he replied. 'Before going inside the lobby, put on a mask and gloves, they are right there,' he said, directing me towards the distribution table. I put on the gloves and the mask to protect myself from infection and we walked into the lobby.

It was a disaster. The entire place smelt really bad. Water was puddled on the floor due to which one could not walk properly. The beautiful, massive artefacts which used to be the talk of the hotel were broken into pieces. The big glass wall right in the front of the entrance was gone. I could see millions of pieces of broken glass on the floor. The entire lobby was crowded with people, mainly hotel staff and officials. But on the positive side, it was really motivating to see that so many people were there to help out. I went to the side just to regain my composure and when I looked down at the floor all I could see was blood flowing under my feet. I could not believe the sight of this beautiful lobby of the flagship hotel of the Taj group in such terrible shape.

'Hey, Ankur!' Victor came up and hugged me as if we were meeting after years.

'Easy, dude, I haven't got transferred yet, nahi jaa raha main abhi,' I said with a smile.

He replied in his typical Parsi accent, 'Ayee, tu bhai hai mera, chal aaja, there are others waiting for you.'

I thought how the hell could they have been waiting for me when even I was not sure whether I was coming or not. Anyway, I went with him. We were right in the middle of the lobby and I could see the group standing around the big round table. My batchmates and colleagues were all there. Looking at me, Vineet smiled and Surender asked, 'Bro, where did you disappear to after we got out?'

Vineet laughed at this and said, 'Now, after a couple of days, is when you are asking this? What if he had died?'

Before I could say anything, Surender commented, 'I am surprised that he hasn't asked me.'

'That's because I knew you went with Vineet to his place and were safe. I would rather have expected you to check on me,' I said.

'Hey Ankur, let's go and at least have a look at the property,' said Victor, to which I agreed.

We crossed the main lobby towards the coffee shop, where the attacks had begun. We went inside Shamiana and saw a prominent bullet hole in the middle of the wooden floor with marks all across. 'Those marks must be from the blast that took place in here,' said Victor.

Right in front was the show kitchen, which was separated from the seating area with a glass window pane. I remembered that a chef was shot while he was working over here. The rest of the place didn't have much lightning, so we decided to go leave.

We took a right turn after coming out to go to Aquarius, the poolside outlet. This had been one of the most beautiful places in the Taj. Sipping a cup of coffee at Aquarius used to be an experience to remember. 'Oh my God, look at the bullets in the pool!' said Victor, pointing his hand.

Moving ahead, we saw the live grills with some meat still on them and the big ice bowl used for chilling beverage cans on a table. Coke cans floated in the water. As we turned to the main dining section of the outlet, I could see a group of commandos lying down on the couches with crossed legs and tetra packs of juice and cans of Coke on the tables.

'Thank you, sirs, you all did a great job, saving many lives,' said Victor.

'Feel free to let us know in case you want something else, like a glass of water, etc.,' I added, at which all of them nodded and smiled.

One of the commandos said, 'No, we don't want anything else. Thanks.'

We were excited to be able to talk to them and acted a bit like kids, eager to get a photograph with them. Finally, we clicked some pictures with them and exited the place.

We went to the Harbour Bar, where the last two terrorists had been shot dead. We came from the the old wing towards the Harbour Bar, crossing the corridor. The entire path was full of bloodstains. This was the same path where I had seen a terrorist for the first time on the night of the twenty-sixth. We went into the bar and had another shock. The entire place was burnt to ashes.

'Hey, this was the table where I was chatting to a guest about malts when it all started,' I told Victor.

The bar counter had nothing left on it—it was now a plain black wall. There used to be a display of the liquor on the wooden cupboard hanging there. The whole place was covered with ash. The only ray of light was coming through the broken windows facing the Gateway of India.

We joined a group of people staring at the spiral staircase which had also been reduced to ashes. When we went forward we realized that the people were not gazing at the staircase, but at the burnt bodies of the terrorists lying under the stairs. For couple of minutes, we could not see the bodies as it was completely dark and it was hard to distinguish the burnt bodies from the ash which covered the floor. All we could see were bones.

On the right hand side of the L-shaped bar the couches had disappeared and it was only the iron skeletons of the tables which had survived.

I don't know what made me do so, but I couldn't control myself and took out my phone and clicked some pictures. Even today, when I see those pictures I get tears in my eyes.

I came out of the Taj and sat on the boundaries of the Gateway, overlooking the ocean. I disconnected every call and ignored all the distractions of the world. I relished the cold breeze, the pleasant weather and the waves of the ocean. I had left home almost four years ago, including my tenure at the hotel management school. I had worked day in day out, but at the moment I could not see the point of this.

Events of the past few days had showed how uncertain life can be. Better to just live every moment as if there is no tomorrow—then at least I would not regret my life coming to an end.

Epilogue

After 29 November, I felt like I had an additional identity. At times, it was a feeling of pride for no reason. At times, it was an extra burden. I think of it as the experience of a lifetime— or perhaps rebirth. I felt I had 'survivor of the Taj attack' tattooed across my face. I did realize that it was not a small thing, but I didn't know exactly how big was.

I came out of my room after a day and met some of my friends and colleagues. They were just not the same—their love and affection was overflowing. The way we used to meet had changed. Small smiles converted into hugs, and it was a different feeling altogether.

I stayed there for a couple of days more to let everything settle down. And since it was Mumbai, a very fast city, it didn't take much time for life to be normal again. People came out of their homes and started going to their offices. Bus services resumed. Even Cafe Leopold, which was also attacked, was opened to the public before the bullet marks could be removed. Just a few days later, the only difference I could see was that the places which had been attacked were under renovation and people came out of their homes to light candles to commemorate the dead. As they say, the show must go on—and I think it always does.

Soon after everything was settled, I booked train tickets as I had too much luggage to take on a plane. I came back to Delhi and, as expected, even this was a different world. The kind affection and respect that came my way was unprecedented. I was overwhelmed by my family's love. My parents didn't inform my grandmother as, according to them, she wouldn't let me go back to Mumbai then. I don't know how they managed to do so, with all the news channels showcasing only the attacks and the phone calls of relatives to ask about my safety.

'You can't go back—either you take a transfer to Delhi or leave your job,' was the first sentence that came out of Mom's mouth as she hugged me. It was a moment filled with rawness. I somehow controlled my tears.

I met friends, relatives and loads of other people. The worst part was that not even one of them referred to me as Ankur any more—their way of introducing me had changed. The standard new introduction was: 'Hey, meet my friend/cousin/ whatever… He is the one who was in the Taj when the attacks took place…' Then the neverending queue of silly questions would begin.

Most of the time, the person to whom I was being introduced wouldn't remember my name but was aware that I was involved in the so-called 'famous' Taj attacks. I also got a call from a journalist at a newspaper's magazine supplement. They wanted to publish my experience of the attacks. And there was something that was eating me from the inside. All I could understand was that though I had survived and was blessed with rebirth, I did not feel good.

After spending a good fifteen days or so at home, finally the time came when I had to head back to Mumbai. I could not avoid it any more. Of course, no one, including me, was happy about me going back to the hotel—rather, to Mumbai.

When I came out of the airport in Mumbai, it felt like there was something missing in the air. I reached my room, put down my baggage and just then I got a call from Mom.

'Hey, beta! Come back,' she said before I could even tell her that I had reached safely. The conversation went on for an hour or so. I remembered the days when I was in Shimla at my hotel school, when I used to literally cry on the phone and Mom used to tell me, 'Baby, don't worry, we are always there, make your future and come back. You won't realize how time flies.' Today, I was trying to convince my mother that time would fly by.

I cried all day and I am sure even Mom was doing the same. That's when I thought again: 'What am I sacrificing? And for what?' I couldn't even keep Mom happy—the person who had sacrificed her entire life for me.

Finally, I went back to the hotel the next day and found that we had to get a new identification card issued from the corporate office. I met my colleagues and understood that work was on and everyone was focusing on the reopening of the property.

The entire area was still a restricted zone, but it made us feel good to show our ID cards and get special entry to the back doors of the hotel. The hotel was supposed to reopen on 21 December, and all those who were caught in the attacks had been called on the 20th. That's when we got to know that we would be doing a red-carpet walk in front of the media and all those special guests who would be invited for the reopening of the property.

Finally, on D-day, we were ready for the guests to walk in. The whole lobby had been redone and the entire top management of the Tatas and the Taj group was at the hotel. Everyone gave their speeches and the planned rituals were carried out. A special platform with a red carpet had been erected for all of us to walk on.

We started walking from the back doors of the hotel. As we were about to reach the main lobby, I could hear the song 'Maa Tujhe Salaam' and the sound of people applauding. I felt a spark of positivity and a sense of pride as I approached the lobby. I could see hundreds of people staring at me and clapping. I could see numerous news cameras from around the world. It was a wonderful feeling.

For that moment, I felt lucky to have been part of the attacks.

Author's Note

After a month or so of the attacks, my mother was not keeping well. I came back to Delhi for around three or four days to visit her. The only thing Mom said was that she wanted me back in Delhi, close to her. This was very unusual for her—she was always the one who taught me and Aditi to go out and take risks. She gave us all the freedom in the world, saying, 'Don't worry, I am standing behind you to catch you even if you fall.' However, this time it was different—she needed me back. It is said that when you really need something it comes to you. And so it happened. After much effort, I got a transfer back to Delhi. I packed up my stuff and rushed back home without even a proper farewell in Mumbai.

After I joined the Taj Mahal Hotel in New Delhi, life started moving at a fast pace. I was working almost sixteen hours a day; the only time I spent with family was my weekly off day. Months passed. Dad got busy getting the house renovated from the scratch. Mom was excited about two things: first, about the house being at its best; second, about Aditi's marriage. She would note down every single thing she liked at other weddings in order to replicate and improve it at Aditi's.

On 26 November 2009, the first anniversary of the attacks, everyone congratulated me on my 'rebirth'. I thanked them all and said a silent prayer for surviving that tragedy by the grace of God and the blessings of my parents.

The day after, 27 November, was a usual day for me. I was working at Wasabi. Mom had gone with my maternal uncle's family to a pre-wedding function. Dad was in Jaipur on a business trip. Then, around eleven, I got a call from my uncle—Mom had met with an accident while crossing the road.

I left everything I was doing, picked up my bike and rode to the hospital as fast as possible. All my relatives were standing outside the gate. My aunt came up to me and said, 'Ankur, your mother is no more.'

People said that this was an accident. That it was meant to be and nobody could change it, etc. That it was a coincidence. I don't believe that.

I was saved during the attacks, when I came so close to death. And exactly one year later, with the entire family on the road, Mom lost her life. I know, in my heart, that she saved me, that she offered herself to the Almighty...

Mom,

I want to tell you that I could not do for you even a bit of what you have done for me. I never wanted to be away from you and wanted you to be always happy. Believe me, it sometimes feels like dying would have been better than living without you. Papa is better now, but at times tears wet his eyes. Aditi is married now and, with your blessings, she is happy. I am a married man as well—my wife is the same girl you always admired. And yes, the house has turned out to be beautiful. All I can offer you now is this book—I dedicate it to you. Thanks for always having been there. And you will always be with me in my heart.

Love you loads and miss you.

—Your son.

Acknowledgements

I would like to thank the people who supported this book with an open heart. First and foremost, my family. Dad and Aditi never disturbed me when I was writing the book. They have supported me time and again, and even after Mom, they never let me miss her. Priya, now my wife, has sacrificed a lot as well. Before we got married, I used to say 'I am feeling sleepy, can't talk any more'—she knew I was busy with something else, but she never asked me any questions and always said goodnight with a smile. Today, when she recounts those moments, we laugh about it. Jitin Chawla, a career counsellor and a very dear friend—he was the biggest motivator for me when it came to writing the book. Rahul Chaudhary, one of the regulars at Wasabi, who guided me through each and every step despite his busy schedule. Last, but most important, Rupa Publications, who said yes to publishing the book when most of the other publishers kept me waiting or said no.

Acknowledgements